Rainwater Harvesting in Arid and Semi-Arid Zones

Rainwater Harvesting in Arid and Semi-Arid Zones

Th.M.Boers

Publication 55

International Institute for Land Reclamation and Improvement,
P.O.Box 45, 6700 AA Wageningen, The Netherlands, 1994

ISBN 90 70754 363 ✓

Printed in The Netherlands

Contents

Preface and Acknowledgements

ILRI was established as a drainage institute and, over the years, has developed expertise in land drainage in arid zones under irrigated agriculture. The principles of land drainage deal with the removal of excess surface water, soil water, and groundwater. The main problem of non-irrigated arid zones is a shortage of water, and it may therefore seem surprising that ILRI should publish a book on rainwater harvesting. Nevertheless, complying with a request from The Netherlands Government through its Directorate General for International Cooperation/*DGIS* in The Hague, to study the possibility of using rainwater harvesting for the development of non-irrigated arid lands, ILRI conducted the study and followed an original approach.

The principles of land drainage to remove excess water were applied to dry lands where there is a shortage of water, but where excess water occurs seasonally, because of high intensity desert storms. In this publication, a procedure has been developed for the design of micro-catchments, each of which consists of a runoff area and a basin area with a tree planted in it. To illustrate the approach, the establishment of windbreaks in Niger and Nigeria was used. The specific objectives of this study are described in the Introduction, along with a brief outline of the contents of each chapter.

This has been a long-term study, covering more than a decade. Its longevity was mainly due to the scarcity of data on the subject. Data from the Institute for Desert Research at Sede Boqer in the Negev Desert were applied to test the approach. Data collected at the ICRISAT Sahelian Centre at Sadoré, Niger, and data from northern Nigeria were used to apply the design procedure in zones where data were scarce. The results for these zones can only be indicative. For actual design, more data from the field are needed, and this publication outlines which data are required.

In rainwater harvesting, two basic processes are important: one is the *inducement and collection of surface runoff* and the other is the *storage and conservation of soil water*. Desert storms produce overland flow, which would normally be evacuated by *surface drainage*, but, in dry lands, this flow can be collected and forced to infiltrate. Excess soil water can be removed by *subsurface drainage* but, in rainwater harvesting, this water is stored and conserved. In this publication, a kinematic-wave approach was applied to model overland flow and the inducement and collection of surface runoff. Alternatively, in the absence of the required data, a runoff-depth model based on linear regression can be applied.

For soil-water flow, or the storage and conservation of soil water, a subsurface drainage model was applied, the numerical soil-water balance model, SWATRE. The combination of surface and subsurface flow models offers a complete solution to the problem. Applying the principles of land drainage to model rainwater harvesting is a logical approach since both are linked in the hydrological cycle and are governed by similar processes such as overland flow on an infiltrating surface and soil-water flow in the presence of root water uptake and deep percolation.

The overall conclusion of this study is that, in arid and semi-arid zones, runoff from small areas such as micro-catchments is an important potential source of water for the establishment, development, and growth of trees. A supply of runoff water can make the difference between death and survival and between minimum development and good growth of trees. Especially in dry years, the runoff water can considerably improve the environmental conditions in which the trees have to grow.

The technology involved is not complicated and can easily be adapted to local conditions of climate, soil, and trees. In many of the areas where rainwater harvesting can be applied, there is a lack of water, wood, food, and shelter, while wind erosion is a major problem. Windbreaks and shelterbelts can serve both the local population and the environment. Once the trees have been planted and the runoff areas have been constructed, only little annual maintenance is needed. This is important for nomads, who are not farmers. Windbreaks demarcate and protect farm land, while large-scale shelterbelts consisting of different types of trees and bushes also serve nomads who do not settle. Rainwater harvesting can also reduce soil erosion by controlling the surface flow. In addition, deep percolation in wet years recharges the groundwater, which can help to redress an upset regional water balance for sound environmental management.

As the author I would like to acknowledge the cooperation I have received from scientists, students, agencies, and ILRI staff while conducting this study and completing this publication. On the application of SWATRE to the problem of rainwater harvesting, I had many discussions with Professor R.A. Feddes of the Wageningen Agricultural University, who reviewed this work. At the outset of this study, I cooperated with Professor J. Ben-Asher of the Institute for Desert Research, Sede Boqer, Israel, and with Dr W.H. van der Molen, Emeritus Professor of the Wageningen Agricultural University. With both scientists, I discussed the use of the kinematic-wave equation to model surface flow.

During this study I drafted papers for international journals and submitted them for critical review. For the papers submitted to the *Journal of Hydrology*, I had an interesting correspondence with its editors, Professor J.E. Nash and Professor J.S.G. McCulloch. The papers I submitted to *Agricultural Water Management* were extensively discussed with its former editors, Dr Ir J. Wesseling and the late Professor N.A. de Ridder. In addition, I had numerous discussions with my co-authors on these and other papers. The review of this work in correspondence and discussions has been a valuable contribution to the scientific and practical content of it.

Every engineer or scientist who is studying the arid zones experiences that scarce rainfall zones are also scarce data zones. Scarcity of storms is aggravated by the extreme scarcity of measurements. For the present study, Ir W.B. Hoogmoed of the Wageningen Agricultural University allowed me to use his data from Niger. I appreciate his readiness to share this data set with me.

I have received much assistance from students who have participated in this study and I have always appreciated their efforts. If I have been demanding in obtaining accurate field measurements, I hope they have learned from this that, in applied hydrological research, there is no alternative. Deserts do not need blackboard hydrology.

I would like to express my appreciation to agencies who have supported my research work. First of all, the Directorate General of International Cooperation in The Hague, who financed the initial stage of the study. Important data to calibrate and test the models originate from the Institute for Desert Research at Sede Boqer, Israel, and I appreciate the support from the staff of that Institute. While working in Nigeria, I appreciated the assistance I received of the European Union Delegation in Lagos. Many consulting bureaux, recognizing the importance of this study for the development of arid zones, opened their libraries to me and asked their field staff to provide whatever data were available. These bureaux were: Haskoning and Euroconsult, The Netherlands; MacDonald Agricultural Services, England; and Hedeselskabet and Danagro Advisor, Denmark.

The former Director of ILRI, Ir F.E. Schulze, agreed to the idea that expertise in land drainage could be applied to the practice of rainwater harvesting. While conducting my research work, I was urged by my former ILRI colleague, the late Professor N.A. de Ridder, to write a solid publication. The present Director of ILRI, Ir M.J.H.P. Pinkers, supported my efforts to complete the study with an ILRI publication. I appreciate that directors and senior staff of ILRI have recognized the importance of continuity to enable me to finalize a long-term study like this one.

Since its establishment, ILRI, in a joint effort with the Winand Staring Research Centre, has built up an excellent library. The first librarian, Ir L.F. Abel, laid the foundation for this dynamic collection and the present librarian, my colleague Ir G. Naber, has continued to improve it. Scientific research is impossible without a good library and, in the field of land and water, the Staring Library is the best in The Netherlands, and quite possibly on this continent. For the present study, I have depended heavily on the library staff and I thank Ir Naber and his team for their efforts.

In producing this publication, I received the cooperation of staff in the Publication Department. The major portion of the English editing was done by Mrs M.F.L. Wiersma-Roche. In spite of the basic English rules Margaret Wiersma has taught us ILRI staff, she had to overhaul an infinite number of my sentences, and I am happy with the reconstruction work. During her absence on a journey to Australia, Mrs M.M. Naeff-Snyder completed the remaining part, and I am grateful to Margaret and Meredith for finishing the work in record time. Mr J. van Dijk drew the figures, sent them to Lahore for review, and did not tire of my requests for corrections. I am very happy with the final result. Mrs J.B.H. van Dillen released an array of Word Perfect macros to get all my symbols right in roman, italic, bold, and subscript. In a scientific publication, even though the subject is practical, the application of basic rules to symbols in equations is a must and I am grateful for the care with which she worked.

Mr J. van Manen took responsibility for the production of this publication and maintained contact with the printer. I am sure I was responsible for some of his headaches, when he had to overhaul his planning, but he did not complain once, at least not in my presence. While at work in Lahore, I made regular phone calls and sent fax messages to keep up to date with how the publication process was proceeding at ILRI. I was happy to learn about arrangements and often depended on information from Mrs V. Ton, secretary to the Director. I appreciate all the efforts that the entire ILRI staff invested in this publication.

Finally, ILRI aims at contributing – by supplementary research – towards a better understanding of the land and water problems in developing countries, and to disseminate this knowledge through publications, courses, and consultancies. I hope this publication will find its way to scientists and engineers who are active in research and development in arid and semi-arid zones. And I hope it will provide some guidance in designing systems for field experiments and development schemes in arid zones. While studying infiltration and surface flow in the field, I became wet on numerous occasions to obtain scarce data. I hope that this publication will not collect dust on a shelf or in a drawer, but that it will become wet and soiled in heavy showers, runoff events, and dust storms in the deserts of this earth.

List of Main Symbols

An attempt has been made to present the main symbols in a coherent format. Where possible, related physical quantities are presented in one group with identical dimensions. Symbols of quantities that fall outside the main line of argument are defined in the text only. Symbols of variables are printed in *italics*, symbols of dimensions appear in Roman type as well as in letters that indicate invariable concepts such as Model (B) or Model (D). Symbols of quantities defined on an annual basis, and some symbols of quantities for surface flow ($\boldsymbol{q}$, $\boldsymbol{m}$, $\boldsymbol{K}$, $\boldsymbol{D_0}$ $\boldsymbol{x_0}$ and $\boldsymbol{t_0}$) are printed in **bold** to distinguish them from similar symbols of different quantities. Bold numbers in brackets refer to chapters.

Symbol quantity		Dimension
A	Runoff plane of area A or runoff area (**1**)	L^2
a	Horton constant (**2**)	T^{-1}
B	Basin area measured at maximum water level (**1**)	L^2
B^*	Horizontal cross-section of wetted soil below basin (**5**)	L^2
b	Depth of water on basin area (**1**)	L
C	Chézy coefficient (**2**)	$L^{1/2}T^{-1}$
c	Celerity or wave speed (**2**)	LT^{-1}
d	Depression storage on runoff area (**2**)	L
$\boldsymbol{D}$	Deep percolation depth below rootzone (annual) (**1**)	L
$\boldsymbol{D^*}$	Deep percolation volume below rootzone (annual) (**6**)	L^3
D	Depth of water on runoff plane (**2**)	L
$D(x,t)$	Depth of water at (x,t) (**2**)	L
D_t	Depth of water at time t on characteristic s (**2**)	L
$\boldsymbol{D_0}$	Depth of water at location $\boldsymbol{x_0}$ and time $\boldsymbol{t_0}$ (**2**)	L
E	Soil evaporation depth (annual) (**1**)	L
E_i	Evaporation depth of intercepted rain (annual) (**1**)	L
E_{act}	Actual soil evaporation depth (annual) (**1**)	L
E_{pan}	Class A pan evaporation depth (annual) (**9**)	L
E_{pot}	Potential soil evaporation depth (annual) (**7**)	L
E_w	Evaporation depth of open water in basin (annual) (**1**)	L
ET_0	Reference evapotranspiration depth (annual)(FAO24*) (**7**)	L
ET_{act}	Actual evapotranspiration depth (annual) (**7**)	L
ET_{pot}	Potential evapotranspiration depth (annual)(FAO24*) (**7**)	L
E_{act}^*	Actual soil evaporation volume (annual) (**6**)	L^3
E	Soil evaporation rate (**4**)	LT^{-1}
E_i	Evaporation rate of intercepted water (**4**)	LT^{-1}

E_{act}	Actual soil evaporation rate (**4**)	LT^{-1}
E_{max}	Maximum possible soil evaporation rate (**4**)	LT^{-1}
E_{pan}	Class A pan evaporation rate (**4**)	LT^{-1}
E_s	Soil evaporation rate according to Black et al. (1969) (**4**)	LT^{-1}
E_{soil}	Soil evaporation rate in Equation (77) (**4**)	LT^{-1}
E_{pot}	Potential evaporation rate of soil (**4**)	LT^{-1}
ET_0	Reference evapotranspiration rate (FAO 24 *) (**4**)	LT^{-1}
ET_{pot}	Potential evapotranspiration rate (FAO 24 *) (**4**)	LT^{-1}
e	Efficiency of micro-catchment (**1**)	–
e_R	Runoff efficiency $e_R = RB/PA$ (**1**)	–
e_U	Water use efficiency $e_U = T_{act}/I$ (**6**)	–
Fr	Froude number $Fr = v/\sqrt{gD}$ (**3**)	–
$f(t)$	Infiltration rate at time t (**2**)	LT^{-1}
f_c	Final infiltration rate of wet soil (**2**)	LT^{-1}
f_i	Initial infiltration rate of dry soil (**2**)	LT^{-1}
g	Acceleration due to gravity (**3**)	LT^{-2}
$h(z,t)$	Soil water pressure head at (z,t) (**4**)	L
h_0	Prescribed soil water pressure head (**4**)	L
I	Infiltration depth in basin (annual) $I = P + R - E_i - E_w$ (**1**)	L
I^*	Infiltration volume in basin (annual) (**6**)	L^3
K	Coefficient in kinematic expression for $m = 1$ (**2**)	LT^{-1}
$K(h)$	Unsaturated hydraulic conductivity (**4**)	LT^{-1}
K_s	Saturated hydraulic conductivity (**5**)	LT^{-1}
K_c	Crop transpiration coefficient for tree (**4**)	–
K_e	Soil evaporation coefficient (**4**)	–
K_{pan}	Pan evaporation factor (FAO 24 *) (**4**)	–
K_{soil}	Evaporation factor of soil (FAO 24 *) (**4**)	–
K_{tree}	Crop evapotranspiration factor for tree (FAO 24 *) (**4**)	–
k	Roughness factor in Chézy coefficient (**2**)	L
L	Losses from rootzone below basin $L = E_{act} + D$ (**1**)	L
L^*	Losses from rootzone below basin (annual volume) (**6**)	L^3
l	Length of runoff plane in direction of flow (**2**)	L
m	Exponent in kinematic depth-flow relation (**2**)	–
n	Manning roughness coefficient (**2**)	$L^{-1/3}T$

P	Rainfall depth (annual) (**1**)	L
P_n	Net rainfall depth (annual) $P_n = P - E_i$ (**1**)	L
P	Rainfall depth (**2**)	L
P_1	Rain storm depth (24 h rainfall) (**2**)	L
$p_{1,n}$	Net rain storm depth (24 h rainfall) (**4**)	L

P^*	Rainfall volume on basin area (annual) (**6**)	L^3

p	Rainfall intensity of one shower (**2**)	LT^{-1}
p_1	Rain storm intensity over one day (**4**)	LT^{-1}

Q	Discharge from runoff plane (**2**)	L^3T^{-1}
Q_{in}	Discharge from plane into weirbox (**2**)	L^3T^{-1}
Q_{out}	Discharge over weir out of weirbox (**2**)	L^3T^{-1}

q	Surface flow rate per unit width of plane (**2**)	L^2T^{-1}
$q(x,t)$	Surface flow rate per unit width at (x,t) (**2**)	L^2T^{-1}
$q_l(t)$	Surface flow rate per unit area at (l,t) (**3**)	LT^{-1}

q	Darcy flux density through soil (**4**)	LT^{-1}
$q(z,t)$	Darcy flux density positive upwards at (z,t) (**4**)	LT^{-1}
$q(-z_b,t)$	Darcy flux density through bottom of profile (**4**)	LT^{-1}
$q_s(0,t)$	Darcy flux density through bottom of basin (**4**)	LT^{-1}

R	Runoff depth (**2**)	L
R	Runoff depth collected in basin area (annual) (**1**)	L
R_1	Runoff depth on area A from 1 rain storm (24 h rain)	L

R^*	Runoff volume collected in basin area (annual) (**6**)	L^3

R_h	Hydraulic radius (**2**)	L
Re	Reynolds number $Re = vD/v$ (**3**)	–

$r(t)$	Rainfall excess rate (**2**)	LT^{-1}

$S(h)$	Volume of soil water taken up by roots per unit bulk volume of soil per unit time (**4**)	T^{-1}
S_{max}	Maximum possible root extraction rate (**4**)	T^{-1}

s_0	Slope of runoff plane (**2**)	–

T	Transpiration depth (annual) (**1**)	L
T_{act}	Actual transpiration depth (annual) (**1**)	L
T_{pot}	Potential transpiration depth (annual) (**7**)	L
T_{target}	Target actual transpiration depth (annual) (**9**)	L

T_{act}^*	Actual transpiration volume (annual) (**6**)	L^3

T	Transpiration rate (**4**)	LT^{-1}
T_{act}	Actual transpiration rate (**7**)	LT^{-1}
T_{max}	Maximum possible transpiration rate (**4**)	LT^{-1}
T_{pot}	Potential transpiration rate (FAO 24 *) (**7**)	LT^{-1}

t	Time (**2**)	T
t_0	Time rain stops and recession starts, Model (C) (**2**)	T
$\boldsymbol{t_0}$	Time point with water depth $\boldsymbol{D_0}$ starts from $\boldsymbol{x_0}$ (**2**)	T
t_c	Time of concentration $t_c = l/v$ (**2**)	T
t_d	Time depressions are full from start of rain (**2**)	T
t_e	Time to peak discharge from start of rain storm (**3**)	T
t_l	Time point at water depth $\boldsymbol{D_o}$ needs to reach $x=l$ (**2**)	T
t_p	Time ponding starts (**2**)	T
t_r	Time rain stops and recession starts, Model (A) (**2**)	T
t_s	Time recession flow stops (**3**)	T

V	Volume of surface water (**3**)	L^3
V_d	Volume of depression storage in one runoff event (**3**)	L^3
V_B	Volume of water in basin after one runoff event (**3**)	L^3
V_I	Volume of infiltration in basin from one runoff event	L^3
V_P	Volume of rainfall on basin of one runoff event (**3**)	L^3
V_R	Volume of runoff in basin from one runoff event (**3**)	L^3

v	Velocity of surface flow (**2**)	LT^{-1}

W	Soil water storage in rootzone below basin (**1**)	L
W_0	Initial soil water storage in rootzone (**7**)	L
W_f	Soil water storage in rootzone at end of year (**7**)	L
W_{max}	Maximum possible soil water storage in rootzone (**1**)	L
$\boldsymbol{W}$	Soil water storage in rootzone (annual) (**1**)	L
$\boldsymbol{\Delta W}$	Soil water storage increase in rootzone (annual) (**1**)	L

w	Width of runoff plane perpendicular to flow (**3**)	L
x	Distance from top of plane in flow direction (**2**)	L
$\boldsymbol{x_0}$	Location of water depth $\boldsymbol{D_0}$ at time $\boldsymbol{t_0}$ (**2**)	L
z	Vertical coordinate from basin bottom positive upwards	L
$|z_b|$	Depth of soil profile below basin area (**4**)	L
$|z_r|$	Depth of rootzone below basin area (**1**)	L

$\alpha(h)$	Root extraction reduction factor (**4**)	–
Γ	Transpiration achievement ratio $\Gamma = T_{act}/T_{target}$ (**9**)	–
δ	Threshold value for surface runoff (**2**)	L
ω	Runoff coefficient (**2**)	–

θ	Soil water content, volume fraction of soil water (**1**)	–
θ_{FC}	Soil water content at Field Capacity (**1**)	–

θ_{WP}	Soil water content at Wilting Point (**1**)	–
θ_0	Initial soil water content (**4**)	–
λ	Soil dependent parameter of evaporation (**4**)	$LT^{-3/2}$
v	Kinematic viscosity (**2**)	L^2T^{-1}
ρ_d	Dry bulk density (**5**)	ML^{-3}
T	Time measured from time depressions are full $T = t - t_d$	T
T_r	Time rain stops measured from t_d, $T_r = t_r - t_d$ (**2**)	T
τ	Time measured from ponding time t_p, $\tau = t - t_p$ (**2**)	T
τ_r	Time rain stops measured from t_p, $\tau_r = t_r - t_p$ (**2**)	T

* FAO 24: Defined according to Doorenbos and Pruitt (1977)

1 Introduction

1.1 Rainwater Harvesting

The problem of water shortage in arid zones is one of low annual rainfall and the unfavourable distribution of rainfall through the year. Under certain conditions, *water harvesting* (i.e. the use of surface runoff for agricultural production) can form a viable complement to irrigated agriculture. Modern water-harvesting research was started in the 1950's by Geddes in Australia. Geddes, as quoted by Myers (1975), gave the first definition of water harvesting:

> 'The collection and storage of any farm waters, either runoff or creek flow, for irrigation use.'

Other definitions that have been given show that water harvesting encompasses methods for *inducing, collecting, storing*, and *conserving* runoff from various sources and for various purposes. The methods applied strongly depend on local conditions and include such widely differing practices as farming terraced wadi beds, growing trees on micro-catchments, tapping subsurface runoff, and storing runoff behind a dam (Boers and Ben-Asher 1980).

In spite of their differences, all these methods have three characteristics in common:
- They are applied in arid and semi-arid regions where runoff has an *intermittent* character. Surface runoff occurs as a discrete event and subsurface water may flow for part of the year and cease flowing during dry periods. Because of the ephemerality of flow, storage is an integral part of water harvesting (Myers 1967);
- They depend upon *local water* such as surface runoff, creek flow, springs, and soaks (Burdass 1975). They do not include the storing of river water in large reservoirs or the mining of groundwater;
- They are relatively *small-scale* operations in terms of catchment area, volume of storage, and capital investment (Myers 1964). This is a logical consequence of the two other characteristics of intermittent flow and local water.

Rainwater harvesting is defined as a method for inducing, collecting, storing, and conserving local surface runoff for agriculture in arid and semi-arid regions (Boers and Ben-Asher 1982). How these four facets of rainwater harvesting interact is illustrated by the micro-catchment in Figure 1.1. A *micro-catchment* is a small catchment, in the order of a few hundred square metres, consisting of a *runoff area* with a maximum flow distance of 100 m and an adjacent *basin area* with a tree, bush, or row crop. The aim of micro-catchment water-harvesting is to induce runoff and collect this water in the basin area, where it is stored and conserved in the rootzone for consumptive use.

Rainfall *induces* surface flow on the runoff area, which preferably has a bare, crusted, and smooth surface. At the lower end of the slope, runoff water is *collected* in the basin area. From the start of rainfall, water will be lost by infiltration in the

1

runoff area, partly in shallow depressions, but also while flowing. Besides runoff water, the basin area also receives direct rainfall, some of which is lost by the evaporation of intercepted rainwater. While the rainfall is infiltrating and the runoff is being collected in the basin area, some water will evaporate from the open water surface, but the major portion infiltrates and is *stored* in the rootzone.

After infiltration has been completed, the next process is the *conservation* of the stored soil water. Water at shallow depth can easily be lost through soil evaporation. Soil water that has infiltrated to a greater depth is safe from evaporation, but may be lost by deep percolation. For the purpose of rainwater harvesting, deep percolation is defined as vertical soil-water flow below the rootzone. From a groundwater point of view, this water can still be a valuable recharge component, but, for the roots, it is considered to be lost. The conserved soil water is available for root water uptake and is used for actual transpiration.

What is illustrated in Figure 1.1 on a small scale occurs in other water-harvesting systems on a larger scale. The relationship of the various components is given by the water-balance equation. For the micro-catchment in Figure 1.1, the water balance of the basin area is important and will be discussed below.

1.2   The Water-Balance Equation

The components of the water balance in the basin area shown in Figure 1.1 can be equated for a defined period of time. For this purpose, a *hydrological year*, consisting of a rainy season and a dry season, is most appropriate. Water balance terms on an annual basis are presented by symbols in bold print. In terms of dimension of water

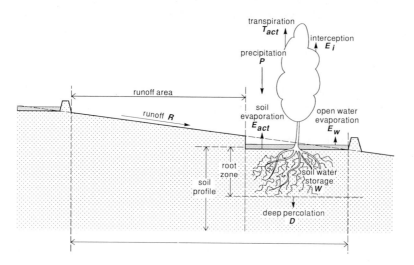

Figure 1.1 Micro-catchment consisting of runoff area and basin area with tree. Rainfall induces runoff, which collects in the basin area, where the water infiltrates, is stored, and is available for root water uptake and transpiration. In the basin area, losses occur by interception, soil evaporation, and deep percolation below the rootzone.

depth in the basin area (L), the annual water balance equation reads (Boers et al. 1986a)

$$T_{act} = P + R - E_i - E_w - E_{act} - D - \Delta W \tag{1}$$

where T_{act} is the actual transpiration, P is the rainfall, R is the depth of runoff calculated over the basin area where it is collected, E_i is the evaporation of water intercepted by the leaves, E_w is the evaporation of open water, E_{act} is the actual evaporation from bare soil, D is the deep percolation below the rootzone, and ΔW is the increase in soil-water storage in the rootzone.

If rainfall occurs during a winter period when trees are without leaves, interception losses can be neglected. But in a climate with summer rainfall and evergreen trees, E_i reduces the rainfall to net precipitation P_n. Open water evaporation, E_w, can often be neglected, because water stands in the infiltration basin only for short periods, of the order of a day. But in general, net precipitation and runoff, minus open water evaporation, together form the total infiltration I:

$$I = P - E_i + R - E_w \tag{2}$$

Actual soil evaporation, E_{act}, and deep percolation, D, make up the losses, L, *from the rootzone*

$$L = E_{act} + D \tag{3}$$

The quantities I and L are sometimes convenient when the result of water-balance predictions are being discussed. For the annual water balance, ΔW can be assumed 0, so that Equation 1 reduces to

$$T_{act} = I - L \tag{4}$$

Equation 4 can be used as a design equation for micro-catchments. In a micro-catchment design for isolated trees (Chapter 6), the water balance is expressed in units of volume, and relevant quantities defined in Chapter 6 are identified as $D*$, $E_{act}*$, $I*$, $L*$, $P*$, $R*$, $T_{act}*$ (L^3). For trees in a windbreak (Chapters 7, 8, 9), units of depth as in Equation 1 are used.

1.3 Runoff Inducement, Collection, Storage, and Conservation

The success or failure of rainwater harvesting depends to a great extent on the quantity of water that can be harvested from an area under given climatic conditions. The threshold retention of a catchment is the quantity of precipitation required to initiate runoff. It depends on various components such as surface storage, rainfall intensity, and infiltration capacity. The *runoff efficiency* of a catchment is the ratio of runoff volume to rainfall volume. Runoff efficiencies, e_R, have been expressed as annual averages to account for variability due to storm size (Fink et al. 1979)

$$e_R = RB/PA \tag{5}$$

where B is the basin area (L^2) and A is the runoff area (L^2).

Sometimes, natural surfaces can yield a good water harvest, e.g. sandstone rock slopes (Chiarella and Beck 1975) or granite outcrops (Burdass 1975). Where such natural surfaces do not exist, measures can be taken to induce runoff. Considerable research has been done on methods to reduce surface storage and to lower infiltration capacity, which are the main parameters that determine threshold retention and runoff efficiency. The methods can be classified as *vegetation removal*, *mechanical surface treatments*, and *chemical surface treatments*.

Vegetation Removal

A summary of studies conducted throughout the world indicates that, in areas with an annual precipitation of more than 280 mm, runoff can be increased by the removal of vegetation (Cooley et al. 1975). With this method, runoff efficiency is low, and may vary greatly per storm, season, or year. The method is usually applied in combination with mechanical surface treatments (Hillel 1967). The main effect of vegetation removal is that it reduces the *infiltration capacity*.

Mechanical Surface Treatment

Mechanical surface treatments, such as *rock clearing* (Evenari et al. 1971), *smoothing* and *compacting* (Frith 1975), are usually done in combination (Anaya and Tovar 1975). The runoff efficiency of catchments is difficult to generalize because it depends on such factors as antecedent soil water, storm intensity, storm duration, catchment size, and the number of years after treatment (Fink et al. 1979). The main effect of surface treatment is that it reduces *surface storage*.

Like vegetation removal, mechanical surface treatment is relatively inexpensive and may last for a long time. Where the dominant factor reducing runoff efficiency is a high infiltration capacity, vegetation removal is more effective than mechanical surface treatment. Where surface storage is the dominant factor, mechanical surface treatment will be more effective.

Chemical Surface Treatment

Many chemicals to reduce infiltration have been tested for water harvesting. The trials cover both preliminary laboratory experiments (Fink 1976) and applications on field scale (Rauzi et al. 1973). Sodium salts, paraffin wax, and asphalt seem to offer good prospects. Sodium salts cause the clay particles in the soil to disperse and partly seal the pores, whereas paraffin wax and asphalt clog the pores themselves. Both reactions reduce the infiltration capacity and increase the runoff. For a more extensive review, see Boers and Ben-Asher (1982).

Runoff Collection

It is a well-known fact that because of reduced infiltration losses, the percentage of runoff increases with a decrease in catchment size (Amerman and McGuinness 1968). Small catchments (1 to 5 ha) can produce runoff amounting to 10 to 15% of the annual rainfall (Figure 1.2). For a micro-catchment (10 to 500 m^2), this can be even higher.

Many runoff collection methods have been developed (National Academy of Sciences 1974). One of them is *micro-catchment water-harvesting*, as was discussed in Section 1.1. The design of a micro-catchment affects water-use efficiency, crop yield, erosion hazard, earth work, and farm operations (Gardner 1975).

The first design factor to consider is micro-catchment size. In experiments, micro-catchment sizes have ranged from roughly 0.5 m^2 (Aldon and Springfield 1975) to

4

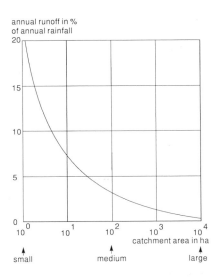

annual runoff in %
of annual rainfall

catchment area in ha

small · medium · large

Figure 1.2 Annual runoff in percentage of annual rainfall as a function of catchment size for small catchment (1 ha), medium-sized catchment (10^2 ha), and large catchment (10^4 ha) (Boers and Ben-Asher 1982).

1000 m^2 (Evenari et al. 1968). Average annual rainfall ranged from 100 mm (Boers et al. 1986b) to 650 mm (Anaya and Tovar 1975).

A second parameter in micro-catchment design is the ratio *runoff-area/basin-area*, which depends on climate, soil conditions, and crop water requirement. In experiments, this ratio has ranged from 1 to 10. A ratio that is too large for the prevailing conditions can result in deep percolation losses. On the other hand, a large ratio promotes infiltration, which reduces direct evaporation losses. The optimum ratio should be found for each set of local conditions (Boers et al. 1986b).

The main advantage of a *micro-catchment* in the order of 100 m^2 is the specific runoff yield as compared with that obtained from, for instance, a *small catchment* of 1 ha, a *medium-sized catchment* of 1 km^2, or a *large catchment* of 100 km^2. The limitation of a micro-catchment is the low crop yield per unit area, even when each crop is producing a high yield per m^3 of water. This is caused by the low number of crops per unit area (Figure 1.3), which also means that farm operations and water are the limiting production factors and not land. Thus, even though micro-catchments show a low potential of crop production per unit area, the potential for the efficient use of water is high.

Soil-Water Storage
Storage, as surface water or soil water, is an integral part of water harvesting (Myers 1975). The decision on how to store water depends in the first place on how the water is to be used. For crop production, surface reservoirs have been used or proposed in a few cases (Smith 1978; Cluff 1979), but soil-water storage is far more common. Figure 1.4 shows Area A, which produces an annual volume of runoff equal to $e_R\mathbf{P}A$. In general, when the runoff volume is large and requires a large storage capacity, surface reservoirs are used. Otherwise soil-water storage is less expensive.

5

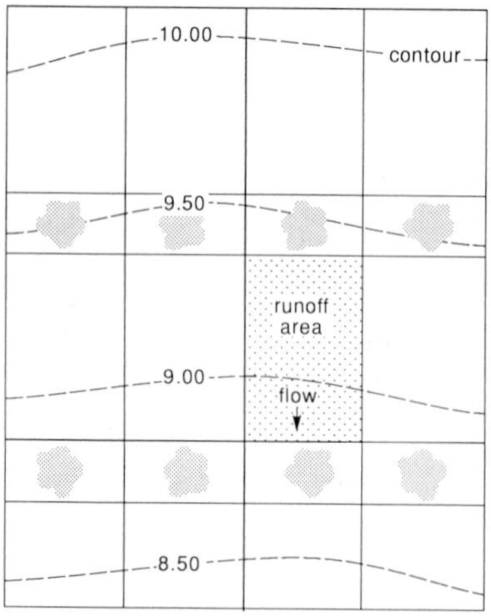

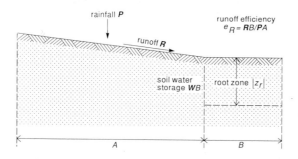

Figure 1.3 Principle of rainwater harvesting from micro-catchments: one option of field layout relative to contour lines, and plan of one micro-catchment (Boers et al. 1986a).

rainfall **P**

runoff efficiency
$e_R = RB/PA$

runoff **R**

soil water
storage **WB**

root zone $|z_r|$

A

B

Figure 1.4 Diagram showing factors determining the volume of surface runoff and the volume of soil-water storage (Boers and Ben-Asher 1982).

The soil-water storage of the rootzone W (L) can be expressed as

$$W = \int_{|z_r|}^{0} \theta \, dz \qquad (6)$$

where θ is the volumetric soil-water content (–), z is the vertical coordinate from the basin area positive upwards (L), and $|z_r|$ is the depth of the rootzone (L).

For the purpose of water harvesting, the maximum possible soil-water storage in the rootzone W_{max} (L) can be approximated by

$$W_{max} \approx (\theta_{FC} - \theta_{WP})|z_r| \qquad (7)$$

where θ_{FC} and θ_{WP} are the volumetric soil-water contents at field capacity and at permanent wilting point, respectively.

The annual runoff volume from Area A results in a runoff depth on Area B equal to $R = e_R PA/B$. According to Equation 2, this leads to infiltration, I. If $I \leq W_{max}$, soil-water storage within the rootzone depth is possible, but if $I > W_{max}$, water may

6

be lost by deep percolation below the rootzone. If $I \gg W_{max}$, surface water storage should be considered.

Soil-Water Conservation
Conserving harvested water by minimizing losses involves reducing soil evaporation and deep percolation (Gardner 1975). Methods have been developed to reduce direct evaporation losses from soil water (Fairbourn 1975; Hoover 1975). In general, the deep storage of soil water and a loosening of the top soil are the best methods to reduce soil evaporation losses. The case of $I > W_{max}$, when deep percolation losses occur, may be due either to rainy years (large I; Rawitz and Hillel 1975) or to a coarse-textured soil (small W_{max}; Ehrler et al. 1978). The best way to reduce deep percolation losses is by maximizing $|z_r|$ (i.e. by selecting a suitable type of tree).

1.4   Purpose and Scope of This Study

The main objective of this study was to develop a design procedure for a water-harvesting system that would be applicable in developing countries, where no previous experience with water harvesting exists. A water-harvesting system suitable for such application should preferably have the following characteristics:
– It should be a *low-cost* system;
– Construction should be possible by *manual labour* with minimal equipment, suitable for self-help schemes;
– Operation and maintenance should be *straightforward* and easy to understand.

On the basis of these criteria, the choice was made for rainwater harvesting from micro-catchments, where runoff is induced on natural surfaces (i.e. without the application of any chemicals). Thus, the *specific purpose of this study* was:

> 'To develop a design procedure for micro-catchments (runoff area and basin area) applicable to environmental and human conditions prevailing in developing countries, such as climate, topography, soils, vegetation, under both nomadic and farming practices.'

The design procedure developed is based on sheet-flow-runoff models and a soil-water-balance model, which together predict the water balance of the rootzone below the basin area of a micro-catchment. This prediction was made for *average, dry, and wet years* and was then repeated for varying sizes of runoff area and basin area. For a given design, the models predict soil-water loss by deep percolation in a wet year, whereas during a dry year, crop water shortage is predicted. The design aims at sufficient soil water being available for a crop in an average year. Deep percolation losses in wet years and water shortages in dry years should then be accepted.

On the runoff area, the important process is to induce and collect runoff. This process is described by a *kinematic-wave model* and a runoff model based on linear regression of runoff depth on storm depth, which for convenience will be referred to as the *runoff-depth model*. Both models predict the runoff collected from given storms. In the basin, soil-water storage and conservation are important. A numerical soil-water-balance model, *SWATRE*, was used to calculate T_{act} and the other terms of the annual rootzone water balance, such as E_{act}, D and ΔW.

Chapter 2 presents the *theory of sheet-flow-runoff models*, which are based on the kinematic-wave theory and linear regression. The models can predict runoff volumes from given storms. The kinematic-wave models assume *constant rainfall intensity*; the runoff-depth model takes storm depth as input. As will be discussed in more detail later (Chapter 3), for the application of the runoff-depth model, the assumption was made in this study that *storm depth* is equal to 24 h rainfall; in other words equal to standard rain-gauge readings.

For four sheet-flow-runoff models, Chapter 3 compares *runoff prediction* and such *model aspects* as model concept, structure, parameters, input requirement, and practical applicability for micro-catchment design. This comparison, which was made with field data from Sede Boqer in the Negev Desert, compares: a kinematic-wave model without depression storage, *Model (A)*; a kinematic-wave model for the rising hydrograph with depression storage, *Model (B)*; a non-linear kinematic recession model, *Model (C)*; and the runoff-depth model, *Model (D)*.

Chapter 4 presents the *theory of SWATRE*, the soil-water-balance model used, including the root water uptake as a function of the soil-water pressure head $S(h)$, initial conditions of the soil-water pressure head $h(z,0)$ and soil-water content $\theta(z,0)$, and upper and lower boundary conditions. The methods that were used to calculate potential rates of transpiration, T_{pot}, and soil evaporation, E_{pot}, from available records of Class A pan evaporation rates, E_{pan}, will be discussed. The approach followed to estimate the evaporation rate of rain intercepted by the leaves, E_i, will also be discussed.

Chapter 5 deals with the *calibration of SWATRE*. Used for this purpose were data on Pistachio trees in micro-catchment basins in Sede Boqer in the Negev Desert, and Pistachio trees in control basins. The materials and methods used for hydrological and soil physical measurements will be described. Calibration was achieved by comparing soil-water storage, W, calculated by SWATRE, with measured W-values.

Chapter 6 discusses *predictions of* $T_{act}*$ in m^3a^{-1} for micro-catchment design in the extremely arid and arid zones of the Negev Desert. For each of these two zones, an average year, a dry year, and a wet year were selected. In the *first series* of predictions, micro-catchment dimensions were the same as those in the experimental field. In the *second series*, the micro-catchment size for the extremely arid zone was increased, and the basin areas in both zones were varied. In the *third series*, $T_{act}*$ in $m^3a^{-1}tree^{-1}$ and yield in $kga^{-1}tree^{-1}$ and in $kga^{-1}m^{-3}$ water were predicted for the arid zone, keeping the basin area constant and increasing the runoff area.

The design predictions were also applied to areas with less marginal rainfall conditions than the Negev Desert, in particular to *semi-arid zones* in Africa ($P \leq$ 800 mm), where a potential for rainwater harvesting on micro-catchments exists. Since a long dry season is common in the semi-arid zones, rainwater harvesting from micro-catchments works best for trees. The extensive root system can draw stored water from a large volume of soil to bridge dry spells. Because, in addition to this, very dry years occur regularly in semi-arid zones, *drought-resistant trees* that can survive these years are required. The application should deal with a problem that is relevant for the semi-arid zones.

The problem selected in this study was the establishment of *Neem windbreaks* in Niger and in northern Nigeria. In northern Nigeria, three large development

8

programmes are being executed by the Government of Nigeria, with the support of the European Union. These programmes include reafforestation components, with the establishment of shelterbelts and windbreaks. They are located in the northwest: Sokoto State (MacDonald 1991); in the central north: Katsina State (Hedeselskabet 1990); and in the northeast: Borno State.

In Niger, many windbreaks have been planted to protect farm land from wind erosion. Various types of trees are used, one of them being the Neem tree, which is suitable for this purpose. An important reason for selecting Neem windbreaks in this study was that at Sadoré, Niger, an *experimental Neem windbreak* was planted in 1984. Research on this windbreak was conducted by the Sahelian Centre of ICRISAT, the Institute for Crop Research in the Semi-Arid Tropics, which has its head office at Patancheru, India. The results of experiments done on that windbreak (Brenner et al. 1991) were used to calibrate the application of SWATRE for this particular purpose.

Chapter 7 deals with the *calibration of SWATRE* on the above-mentioned experimental Neem windbreak at Sadoré, in the semi-arid zone of Niger. The design of this experimental windbreak will be presented (i.e. type and spacing of trees, row distance, and planting pattern). Initial and boundary conditions for SWATRE will be discussed, as well as parameter values required to calculate E_i, T_{pot}, and E_{pot}. The soil-water retention characteristic, $h(\theta)$, and hydraulic conductivity function, $K(\theta)$, used for Sadoré will be presented. For calibration, T_{act}-values as determined from sap flux measurements by Brenner et al. (1991) were compared with the values of T_{act} calculated by SWATRE.

Chapter 8 compares *the runoff prediction* by the kinematic-wave model with depression storage, *Model (B)*, and the runoff-depth model, *Model (D)*, using data from Niamey, Niger (for location, see Figure 1.5a). Thirteen years of rainfall data were routed through both models. Predicted runoff volumes were used to calculate runoff efficiencies, which were compared with values from literature. This comparison was used to set values of model parameters for runoff prediction with *Runoff Depth Model (D)*.

From the thirteen years of rainfall records, an average year, a dry year, and a wet year were selected. For these three years, T_{act} *was predicted* by SWATRE for: (1) runoff predicted by the Kinematic Wave Model (B), and (2) runoff predicted by Runoff Depth Model (D). Design criteria in terms of lower T_{act}-limits were developed and the *result of prediction was compared* for both cases.

Chapter 9 deals with *predictions of T_{act}* for micro-catchment design in four locations from which rainfall data were available: *Sadoré, Tahoua, Sokoto, and Katsina* (*Niamey* is dealt with in Chapter 8). Figure 1.5a indicates an area of 1,000,000 km² surrounding the 5° east meridian, between the 20th and 10th parallels. The central area (Niamey, Sadoré, Tahoua) and the northeast (Agadez, Iferouane) are located in Niger. Mali is in the northwest (Kidal, Menaka), Burkina Faso and Benin (Malanville) are in the southwest, and Nigeria (Sokoto, Katsina) is in the southeast.

The River Niger – the Black Nile – enters Niger from Mali northwest of Niamey, and leaves Niger near Gaya. In the north, the Niger sub-desert extends into wide expanses towards the Sahara Desert, where annual rainfall drops below 100 mm. It is assumed that at the 20th parallel rainfall has become negligible. Figure 1.5b indicates a number of weather stations in Niger and Nigeria and their approximate distances

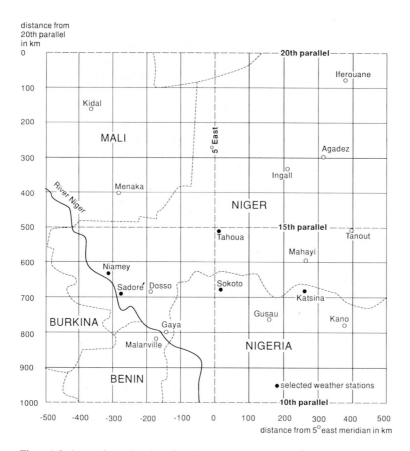

distance from
20th parallel
in km

distance from 5° east meridian in km

Figure 1.5a Approximate location of weather stations relative to 5° east meridian (indicated at 0 km) between the 20th and 10th parallels. The weather stations selected for this study are indicated by black dots. North of the 20th parallel, annual rainfall is assumed to be negligible.

to the 20th parallel. The vertical scale carries the average annual rainfall **P**. Going from the 20th parallel to the 10th parallel, the average annual rainfall increases first by *50 mm/100 km*. The rainfall gradient steepens to *200 mm/100 km* near the 10th parallel.

The area near the 10th parallel borders on a region where trees grow well on rainwater only. Towards the north, rainwater becomes increasingly scarce and harvesting it as runoff water would be beneficial. Data were available from a few weather stations in the *transition zone from rainfall forestry to rainwater-harvesting-based forestry*: Katsina (**P** is 552 mm), Sokoto (**P** is 536 mm), Sadoré (**P** is 522 mm), and Tahoua (**P** is 335 mm). North of Tahoua, there is also a potential for rainwater-harvesting-based forestry. Design predictions were made for a Neem windbreak as at Sadoré (Chapter 7). The degree to which the design criteria are met was quantified by *transpiration achievement ratio Γ*, defined as $\Gamma = T_{act}/T_{target}$. Data were analyzed for weather and soil conditions.

Chapter 10 summarizes the findings of this study. Essential elements in the

10

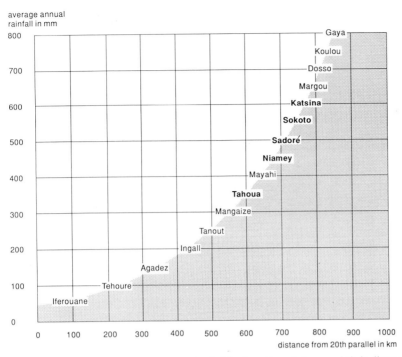

Figure 1.5b Approximate average annual rainfall of weather stations and their distances from the 20th parallel (see Figure 1.5a), north of which rainfall is assumed to be negligible. In this study, micro-catchment design predictions were made with the use of rainfall data from the weather stations with names printed in bold.

rainwater-harvesting equation are reviewed: seasonal distribution of rainfall soil hydraulic conditions, and tree hydrological/physiological characteristics. Efficiencies of runoff and water use are discussed. Future applications are discussed, in terms of the establishment, development, and growth of trees. In the area near the 10th parallel, trees grow on rainfall, but more water might improve their growth. In the area near the 20th parallel, trees surviving on rainfall could do better if more water were available. If rainwater harvesting could advance the building of windbreaks and shelterbelts, *this would serve farmer, nomad, and the environment.*

2 Theory of Sheet-Flow-Runoff Models

2.1 The Kinematic-Wave Equation

Consider a flow over a sloping plane of length l and a smooth surface (i.e. without a concentrated flow in rills or gullies), and take the x-axis along the plane, so that $x = 0$ represents the top of the plane, and $x = l$ the downslope end. The lateral and upstream boundaries of the plane are formed by impervious borders, which close the plane to any upstream or lateral flow. The lower boundary is formed by a gutter, where runoff is collected and recorded. The geometry of the system is shown in Figure 2.1. The continuity equation follows from the *water-balance of a control volume* with a length dx

$$\text{Flow into control volume} = q - (\partial q/\partial x)dx/2 + pdx \tag{8}$$

$$\text{Flow from control volume} = q + (\partial q/\partial x)dx/2 + fdx \tag{9}$$

$$\text{The increase of storage} = (\partial D/\partial t)dx \tag{10}$$

where q is the flow rate per unit width of plane $(L^3 T^{-1} L^{-1})$, p is the rainfall intensity (LT^{-1}), f is the infiltration rate (LT^{-1}), D is the flow depth (L), x is the distance from the top of the plane (L), and t is the time (T).

The water balance of the control volume (Equation 8 – Equation 9 = Equation 10) gives

$$-(\partial q/\partial x)dx + pdx - fdx = (\partial D/\partial t)dx \tag{11}$$

Introducing the rainfall excess $r(t)$ (LT^{-1})

$$r(t) = p(t) - f(t) \tag{12}$$

and dividing by dx gives the *continuity equation*

$$\partial D/\partial t + \partial q/\partial x = r(t) \tag{13}$$

Applying the *kinematic depth-flow approximation*

$$q = K D^m \tag{14}$$

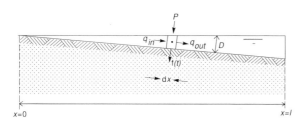

Figure 2.1 Sloping plane of length l with sheet flow of depth D. Continuity equation is derived from the water balance of a control volume dx with net lateral inflow $p-f(t)$ (Boers et al. 1994).

where K is a constant associated with surface roughness and slope and m is a constant depending on the flow regime. The dimension of K (length$^{(2-m)}$time^{-1}) depends on the value of m.

The applicability of Equation 14 is based on the following considerations. Unsteady flow in open channels, including flow over a smooth sloping plane, can be described by the non-linear Saint-Venant equations: a momentum equation and a continuity equation. The main requirements for the applicability of these equations are conditions of a gradually varied flow, a hydrostatic pressure distribution, a small slope, and the absence of deceleration losses.

An analytical solution to these partial differential equations is not known, and a kinematic solution is a practical alternative. Under the conditions specified above, the magnitude of the inertia terms and the hydrostatic pressure gradient can be assumed to be negligible in comparison with the bottom slope and friction slope. This assumption leads to the kinematic-wave approach, in which *parameter estimate* replaces the physical modelling.

Substituting Equation 14 into Equation 13 gives the *kinematic-wave equation*

$$\partial D/\partial t + \partial KD^m/\partial x = r(t) \tag{15}$$

This is a first-order partial differential equation, the degree of which depends on the value of m.

2.2 Kinematic-Wave Model without Depression Storage: Model (A)

For turbulent flow, the *Chézy equation* applies, with the hydraulic radius R_h equal to D for overland flow

$$q = vD = CD^{3/2}s_0^{1/2} \tag{16}$$

with

$$C = 18 \log 12D/k \tag{17}$$

where v is the flow velocity (LT^{-1}), C is the Chézy coefficient (L$^{1/2}$T^{-1}), s_0 is the bottom slope (–), and k is the roughness factor (L).

A comparison of Equations 14 and 16 shows

$$K = Cs_0^{1/2} \tag{18}$$

and $m = 3/2$ for *turbulent flow*.

When the *Manning equation* for overland flow is used

$$q = vD = (1/n)D^{5/3}s_0^{1/2} \tag{19}$$

where n is the roughness coefficient (L$^{-1/3}$T).

14

From Equations 14 and 19, it follows that

$$K = (1/n)s_0^{1/2} \qquad (20)$$

and $m = 5/3$ for *turbulent flow* (Linsley et al. 1982).

The use of the *Poiseuille equation* for laminar flow gives

$$q = vD = (gs_0/2v)D^3 \qquad (21)$$

where g is the acceleration due to gravity (LT^{-2}) and v is the kinematic viscosity (L^2T^{-1}). From Equations 14 and 21, it follows that

$$K = gs_0/2v \qquad (22)$$

and $m = 3$ for *laminar flow* (Henderson and Wooding 1964).

Zarmi et al. (1983) assumed that, under the conditions on the plane, a value of $m = 1$ in Equation 14 is justified. This gives $q = KD$, and since for overland flow we have $q = vD$, this implies $K = v$. The physical concept behind this assumption of *constant flow velocity* seems reasonable for overland flow during rainfall, as may be seen from the following.

The length of the plane under consideration is limited to a few tens of metres, and the average flow depth will be a few millimetres. This means that the average thickness of the water layer is of the same order as the raindrop diameter (see Figure 2.2).

Figure 2.2 describes schematically that when a raindrop strikes the thin water layer, the impact will stop a water particle at the place of collision. Downstream of this location, the flow continues at the same rate. So the continuity of the flow lines is disturbed. After the impact, the water particle will accelerate again until it collides with the next falling raindrop. The acceleration between two collisions is low because the surface slope is small and the flow is dominated by friction forces between the thin water layer and the soil surface. These effects make it reasonable to assume a constant average flow velocity during *disturbed flow under rainfall* (see Figure 2.3).

This assumption of $m = 1$ linearizes Equation 15, which can then be solved analytically. Zarmi et al.(1983) used the Horton infiltration model for $f(t)$, which is applicable for infiltration into *crust-forming bare soils* (Morin and Benyamini 1977)

$$f(t) = f_c + (f_i - f_c)e^{-at} \qquad (23)$$

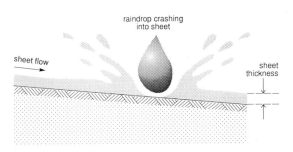

Figure 2.2 Disturbance of sheet flow by raindrop striking the thin water layer. Sheet thickness and raindrop diameter have the same order of magnitude (Boers et al. 1994).

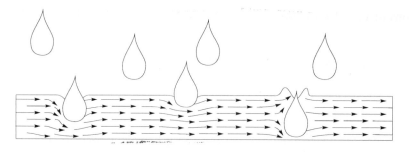

Figure 2.3 Sketch of raindrop impact on thin water layer. The collision of the raindrop with flowing water particles stops the particles. After the collision, the particles will start moving again. These collisions cause disturbed flow conditions, and the assumption of constant average flow velocity can be made.

where $f(t)$ is the infiltration rate at time t (LT^{-1}), f_i is the initial infiltration rate of dry soil (LT^{-1}), f_c is the constant infiltration rate of wet soil (LT^{-1}), and a is the Horton constant (T^{-1}).

For constant p and with Equation 23, the rainfall excess in Equation 15 is known. For initially dry conditions, the rainfall will normally infiltrate until the infiltration rate drops to the rainfall intensity, at ponding time t_p. Subsequently, setting $\tau = t-t_p$ and with the assumption $\boldsymbol{m} = 1$, Equation 15 is written as

$$\partial D/\partial \tau + v\partial D/\partial x = r(\tau) \tag{24}$$

The following initial and boundary conditions apply to Equation 24

Initial condition (*dry start*): $D(x,\tau) = 0, \tau = 0, x \geq 0$ (25a)

Boundary condition (*dry top*): $D(x,\tau) = 0, x = 0, \tau \geq 0$ (25b)

The solution of Equation 24, subject to the conditions of Equations 25, is shown in Figure 2.4a for rising hydrograph, plateau, and recession curve (Zarmi et al. 1983). The *rising hydrograph* consists of two parts

$$D(x, \tau) = (p-f_c)\tau - [(p-f_c)/a][1-e^{-a\tau}] \qquad \text{for: } \tau \leq x/v \tag{26a}$$

$$D(x, \tau) = (p-f_c)x/v - [(p-f_c)/a][e^{-a(\tau-x/v)}-e^{-a\tau}] \qquad \text{for: } \tau > x/v \tag{26b}$$

The *plateau of the hydrograph* is

$$D(x,\tau) = (p-f_c)x/v \qquad \text{for } \tau \gg x/v \tag{26c}$$

At $\tau = \tau_r$, rain stops, where $\tau_r = t_r-t_p$. The *recession curve* is

$$D(x,\tau) = (p-f_c)x/v - p(\tau-\tau_r) \qquad \text{for: } \tau > \tau_r \tag{26d}$$

The flow rate per unit width of plane is $\boldsymbol{q} = vD$, with D from Equations 26.

2.3 Kinematic Rising Limb with Depression Storage: Model (B)

The solution of Zarmi et al.(1983) is valid from the time of ponding t_p. This means that, according to their model, surface flow starts at $t = t_p$, (Figure 2.4), which implies the absence of any depression storage. Boers et al.(1994) have presented a solution which includes depression storage.

For initially dry conditions, the rainfall infiltrates until the infiltration rate drops to the rainfall intensity, after which depressions will begin to be filled, and later surface detention is built up and runoff begins. The effect of depression storage may be modelled as a *threshold or storage* which must be reached before surface detention begins. For infiltration on a dry crusted surface under constant rainfall starting at time $t = 0$, we apply Equation 23. Assuming $p < f_i$, then

$$f(t) = p; \qquad\qquad\qquad t \le t_p \qquad\qquad\qquad (27a)$$
$$f(t) = f_c + (f_i - f_c)e^{-at}; \qquad t > t_p \qquad\qquad\qquad (27b)$$

The ponding time, t_p, follows from

$$t_p = -(1/a)\ln(p - f_c)/(f_i - f_c) \qquad\qquad\qquad (28)$$

After ponding time, the storage in closed depression d (mm) will be filled. Assume that this process is completed at $t = t_d$, then for $t > t_d$, flow begins (Figures 2.5a and 2.5b).

For $t_p < t < t_d$, the water balance is: rainfall depth = depression storage + infiltration depth

$$(t_d - t_p)p = d + \int_{t_p}^{t_d} f(t)dt \qquad\qquad\qquad (29)$$

Substituting Equation 23 into Equation 29 and integrating with Equation 28 gives

$$(t_d - t_p) = d/(p - f_c) + (1/a)[1 - e^{(t_d - t_p)}] \qquad\qquad\qquad (30)$$

The parameters reflecting soil properties in Equation 30 are a and f_c. In this model, depression storage d is a function of surface roughness: a rough surface has a high d-value. From Equation 30, t_d is found by an iterative process (see Section 3.1).
In Equation 15, rainfall excess $r(t)$ is now given by

$$r(t) = p - f(t); \qquad\qquad\qquad t \le t_p \text{ and } t \ge t_d \qquad\qquad\qquad (31a)$$
$$r(t) = p - f(t) - dt/(t_d - t_p); \qquad t_p < t < t_d \qquad\qquad\qquad (31b)$$

In Equation 31b, $d/(t_d - t_p)$ is the rate at which depressions are filled.
Equation 15 should now be solved for $t \ge t_d$, or with
$T = t - t_d$, for $T \ge 0$, and with $m = 1$ as in Equation 24. Hence the initial condition (IC) and boundary condition (BC) are

$$\text{IC } (\textit{depressions full}): D(x,T) = 0, T = 0, x \ge 0 \qquad\qquad\qquad (32a)$$

$$\text{BC } (\textit{dry top of slope}): D(x,T) = 0, x = 0, T \ge 0 \qquad\qquad\qquad (32b)$$

Some doubt has been raised as to the validity of Condition 32b for moderate to gently

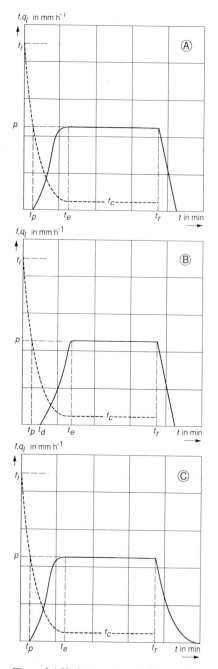

Figure 2.4 Hydrographs of runoff on micro-catchment under constant storm intensity for Models (A), (B), and (C).

Figure 2.4a Model (A) (Zarmi et al. 1983): Flow starts at ponding time t_p, reaches plateau at t_e, and recession after storm is linear.

Figure 2.4b Model (B) (Boers et al. 1994): Depression storage delays the time when flow starts t_d and time to plateau t_e. Linear recession is identical to Model (A).

Figure 2.4c Model (C) (Boers et al. 1994): Rising hydrograph and plateau are identical to Model (A). Recession is non-linear because of the transition to turbulent flow conditions.

18

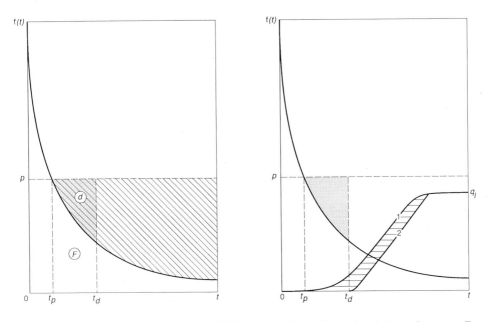

Figure 2.5a Infiltration f(t) under constant rainfall p. Potential runoff is the hatched area for $t > t_p$. For $t_p < t < t_d$, Area d is the depression storage and Area F is the infiltration. Actual runoff equals potential depth minus depression storage (Boers et al. 1994).

Figure 2.5b Depressions fill between t_p and t_d. Without depressions, flow starts at t_p; Case 1 is Model (A). With depressions, flow starts at t_d; Case 2 is Model (B). The area between Hydrographs 1 and 2 (hatched) is the difference in runoff, which equals the depression storage (shaded) (Boers et al. 1994).

sloping watersheds (Singh 1978). This was investigated in the laboratory by de Lima and Torfs (1990) for various rainfall intensities on a plane with a slope varying from 0.001 to 0.04. Applying the result of their study to the 0.01 sloping plane used in the present study shows that $D(0,T) < 0.1$ mm. From this result, it was concluded that, in this case, Equation 32b is a *valid boundary condition*.

Setting $C = (f_i - f_c) e^{atd} = (p - f_c) e^{-a(td - tp)}$ and $A = (p - f_c)$ (33)

The rainfall excess in Equation 15 is then written as

$$r(T) = A - Ce^{-aT} \qquad (34)$$

Equation 15 with Equation 34 and $\boldsymbol{m} = 1$ is solved through the Laplace Transformation (see Appendix A1). The solution for the *rising hydrograph* is (see Figure 2.4b)

$$D(x,T) = AT - (C/a)[1 - e^{-aT}] \qquad \text{for: } T \le x/v \qquad (35a)$$

$$D(x,T) = A(x/v) - (C/a)[e^{-a(T - x/v)} - e^{-aT}] \qquad \text{for: } T > x/v \qquad (35b)$$

where x/v is the time required to cover distance x. For $x = l$, this is the time of concentration, t_c (T).

From Equation 35, the flow rate per unit width of plane is found as $\boldsymbol{q} = vD$ (L²T⁻¹). For $d = 0$, we have in Equation 33, $t_p = t_d$ and $A = C = (p - f_c)$. Substitution of

19

this condition reduces Equations 35a and 35b to Equations 26a and 26b, the solution of Zarmi et al.(1983).

The *plateau of the hydrograph* is given by

$$D(x,T) = (p-f_c)x/v \qquad (35c)$$

If we assume that rainfall stops at $t = t_r$, or at $T = T_r$, with $T_r = t_r-t_d$, we find the *recession* in Equation 26d to be

$$D(x,T) = (p-f_c)x/v - p(T-T_r) \qquad \text{for: } T > T_r \qquad (35d)$$

The model predicts a linear recession curve, starting from $(p-f_c)x/v$ with slope p (Figures 2.4a and b). Field measurements have shown deviations of the actual recession curve from the linear prediction. It was checked whether this could be caused by the weir and the storage in the weirbox (see Figure 2.6), but the result was negative. The *weir and weirbox introduce a small time lag*, but conserve the shape of the recession curve (Boers et al. 1991). A more probable explanation is that, after the rainfall has stopped, the flow regime changes and the value of **m** can no longer be assumed 1 (see below, Model (C)).

2.4   Non-Linear Kinematic Recession Model: Model (C)

During the recession, there is no raindrop impact, the flow is no longer disturbed, and the flow rate depends on the water depth. The assumption of constant velocity

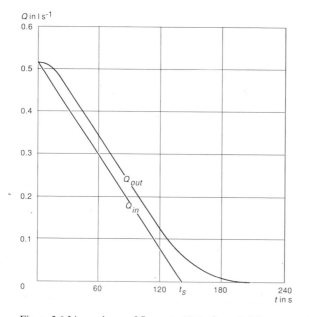

Figure 2.6 Linear decay of flow rate (Q_{in}) after rainfall stops, and resulting discharge (Q_{out}) over weir as calculated with predictor-corrector method. For $t > t_s$, $Q_{in} = 0$, and Q_{out} comes from the weirbox only (Boers et al. 1991).

20

loses its validity, and this may explain why the measured recession of the flow rate deviates from the linear recession curve. The disturbed flow is followed by a *transition phase* in which flow velocity can increase. This means that the value of **m** increases (Boers et al. 1994).

This concept suggests that a non-linear recession model fits the data better. A non-linear solution (Figure 2.4c) of Equation 15 can be obtained through the *method of characteristics*, replacing Equation 15 by two ordinary differential equations (Parlange et al. 1981)

$$\mathrm{d}x/\mathrm{d}t = c = \boldsymbol{m}\boldsymbol{K}\boldsymbol{D}^{m-1} \tag{36}$$

and

$$\mathrm{d}D/\mathrm{d}t = r(t) \tag{37}$$

where c is the celerity or wave speed (LT^{-1}).

Solving Equation 36 yields an expression for the *characteristics* in the x,t plane, whereas Equation 37 gives the *trajectories* in the D,t plane. If we assume a constant net supply rate $p - f(t)$, the location of the principal characteristic (from $x = 0$, $t = 0$ at start of flow) in the x,t plane follows from integrating Equation 36 and is given by

$$x = \boldsymbol{K}r^{m-1}t^{m} \tag{38}$$

This characteristic divides that plane (see Figure 2.7) into two regions, in one of which (I) the *flow is uniform* (not changing with x) and is completely characterized by

$$D = rt \tag{39}$$

which follows from integrating Equation 37. In the other region (II), the *flow is steady* and completely characterized by

$$\boldsymbol{q} = rx \tag{40}$$

Equations 39 and 40 provide the complete solution to the problem. The depth along the characteristic s is found by inserting t from Equation 39 into Equation 38, yielding

$$D^{m} = rx/\boldsymbol{K} \tag{41}$$

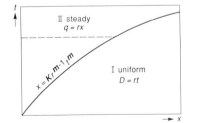

Figure 2.7 Diagram of x,t plane, showing principal characteristic, which divides the plane into two regions. In Region I, the flow is *uniform* (not changing with x); in Region II, the flow is *steady* (not changing with t). The dotted line represents the instant that rainfall stops and recession starts (Boers et al. 1994).

Numerical Solution for the Recession Curve

The dotted line in Figure 2.7 represents the instant at which the storm ends and recession starts. This means that from that time onwards, $(t=t_0=0)$: $p = 0$ and $r(t) = -f_c$. Integrating Equation 37 between the limits $(D_0, t_0 = 0)$ and (D_t, t) gives for the decrease of D along the characteristic s

$$D_t = D_0 - f_c t \qquad (42)$$

For the wave speed, substituting Equation 42 into Equation 36 gives

$$dx/dt = mK(D_0 - f_c t)^{m-1} \qquad (43)$$

Initial conditions with $p > 0$ follow from Equation 40. It is assumed that the rainfall intensity p is constant, and that the final infiltration rate f_c has been reached. So there is equilibrium between net lateral inflow $(p-f_c)x$ and outflow q

$$(p-f_c)x = KD^m \qquad (44)$$

If we assume $x = x_0$ at $t = t_0 = 0$, Equation 43 yields

$$x_0 = KD_0^m / (p-f_c) \qquad (45)$$

Equation 45 describes the shape of the water surface $D_0(x_0)$ in equilibrium at $t = 0$. Figure 2.8 gives a sketch of this situation for the plane per unit width of 1 m. The position of a point x where the depth is D_0 and which starts moving at time $t = t_0 = 0$ with the velocity of the kinematic wave is given by

$$x = x_0 + \int_0^t dx/dt \, dt \qquad (46)$$

The integral in Equation 46 is the distance covered up to time t.

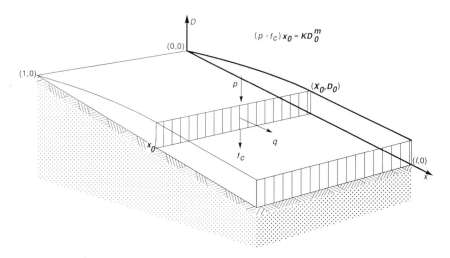

Figure 2.8 Sheet flow in equilibrium over plane of length l per unit width of 1 m, with an arbitrary point of the water surface (x_0, D_0). The net lateral inflow over x_0: $(p-f_c)x_0$ equals the flow downstream of x_0: $q = KD_0^m$; see Equation (44) (Boers et al. 1994).

22

Substituting Equation 43 into Equation 46 gives

$$x = x_0 + \int_0^t mK(D_0 - f_c t)^{m-1} dt \tag{47}$$

The solution of Equation 47 will allow the calculation of the propagation of a point x with water depth D_0 in the kinematic wave. With dummy variable u, we put

$$u = D_0 - f_c t, \text{ so: } du/dt = -f_c, \text{ or: } dt = -du/f_c \tag{48}$$

$$\text{For } t = 0: \quad u = D_0 \tag{49a}$$

$$\text{For } t = t: \quad u = D_0 - f_c t \tag{49b}$$

With Equations 48 and 49, it follows from Equation 47

$$x = x_0 + \int_{u = D0}^{u = D0 - fct} mK u^{m-1}(-du/f_c) = x_0 - (K/f_c) \left[u^m \right]_{u = D0}^{u = D0 - fct} \tag{50}$$

or

$$x = x_0 + (K/f_c)[D_0^m - (D_0 - f_c t)^m] \tag{51}$$

with x_0 given by Equation 45.

The *recession curve* is described by Equations 51 and 45, which leads to a numerical solution of Equation 15. For a given value of wave depth D_0, Equation 45 gives the location x_0 of this depth at the start of recession, $t = 0$. For $x = l$, Equation 51 gives the time t_l, required for the point where wave depth at the start is D_0 to move from $x = x_0$ to $x = l$. During this time, water depth at $x = l$ reduces according to Equation 42, which gives $D(l,t_l)$. With $D(l,t_l)$, discharge $q(l,t_l)$ follows from Equation 14. (For a solved numerical example, see Appendix A2.)

If we take $t = \tau_r + t_d$, the linear recession of Zarmi et al. (1983), Equation 26d follows from Equation 51 with $m = 1$, Equations 45 and 42.

2.5   Linear Regression Storm-Runoff-Depth Model: Model (D)

Rainfall and runoff are of short duration and can be regarded as bursts. Field data indicate that the rainfall-runoff relationship can be described by a linear regression model. This model does not take into account the effect of rainfall intensity on the runoff process. The linear regression model has been applied to annual rainfall and runoff data from *large and small catchments* by Diskin (1970), Diskin et al. (1973), and to *separate storms* by Fink et al. (1979), and Boers et al. (1986a).

The basis for using the model to describe the relationship between rainfall and runoff from micro-catchments, as has been done in the present study, is the following. By reducing the scale of time from one year to one storm, and by reducing the scale of space from a large catchment to a micro-catchment, many storm runoff data can be collected during one or two rainy seasons from a number of micro-catchments. These data can then be used (a) to check whether the model is applicable on *reduced scales of time and space*, and (b) to evaluate the *model parameters*.

23

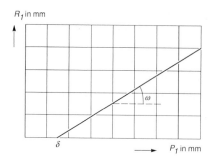

Figure 2.9 Runoff Depth Model (D): Linear regression of runoff depth R_l on storm depth P_l, with runoff coefficient ω and threshold value δ (Boers et al. 1986a).

For separate rain storms, the *runoff-depth model* can be written as (see Figure 2.9)

$$R_1 = 0 \qquad \text{for} \quad 0 \le P_1 \le \delta \qquad (52a)$$
$$R_1 = \omega(P_1 - \delta) \quad \text{for} \qquad P_1 > \delta \qquad (52b)$$

where P_l is rain storm depth (L), R_l is storm runoff depth (L), ω is the runoff coefficient (–), and δ is the runoff threshold (L).

The assumption was made that rain storm depth equals 24 hours rainfall depth (see Chapter 3).

3   Comparison of Sheet-Flow-Runoff Models at Sede Boqer

3.1   Experimental Set-up and Methods of Data Analysis

The sheet-flow-runoff models (A), (B), (C), and (D) discussed in Chapter 2 were applied to catchments and micro-catchments of the Institute for Desert Research/IDR at Sede Boqer in the Northern Negev Desert, Israel (Zarmi et al. 1983; Boers et al. 1994). The first part of this section deals with experiments used to compare Models (A), (B), and (C). After this, measurements for Model (D) will be discussed. To apply Models (A), (B), and (C), surface flow was generated by natural rainfall and with a simulator that produced rainfall of constant intensity on a plane surrounded by impervious borders (Table 3.1). The experimental field of the Institute for Desert Research will be described in Chapter 5.

The soil in the experimental field is a clay loam of aeolean origin, which was deposited as a loess cover with a particle size of which 90% by weight was finer than 70 μm. The surface of the plane was bare, crusted, without deep depressions, and sloping 1 to 2%. Runoff was monitored with a 90° Thomson weir and a water-level recorder at the downstream end of the plane. Rainfall was measured with standard and recording rain gauges (Figure 3.1).

Measurements to Compare Model (B) with Model (A): The Effect of Depression Storage on the Rising Hydrograph
For each of the four experiments used for this comparison (Table 3.1), *time to ponding*, t_p, followed from Equation 28, while time to fill depressions, t_d, was found from Equation 30 by an iterative procedure.

Let $y = t_d - t_p$, then Equation 30 becomes

$$y = d/(p-f_c) + (1/a)[1-e^{-ay}] \tag{53}$$

For short periods of time, the solution can be expanded in a Taylor series: $1-\exp(-ay) \approx ay - a^2 y^2/2$. Substitution into Equation 53 leads to the first estimate of y

$$y_I = [2d/a(p-f_c)]^{1/2} \tag{54}$$

Table 3.1 Characteristics of catchments and parameter values of the four rainfall-runoff events used (Boers et al. 1994)

	lxw mxm	d mm	a s^{-1}	f_c mm h^{-1}	p mm h^{-1}	t_p s	t_d s	v m s^{-1}
1 SR	12.50 × 10.00	0.2	0.008	4.8	59.4	120	180	0.08
2 NR	12.00 × 10.50	0.2	0.010	3.4	48.0	90	150	0.08
3 SR	12.00 × 10.50	0.2	0.008	7.6	25.8	120	240	0.04
4 NR	18.00 × 14.00	0.2	0.004	4.1	10.5	420	690	0.05

SR = Simulated Rainfall, NR = Natural Rainfall

25

Figure 3.1 Catchment area of 125 m^2 during experiment with rainfall simulator suspended on cables over the area. Surface runoff collects in gutter at downstream end and is measured with a Thomson weir and a water-level recorder. Rainfall is measured with small tube gauges spread over the area.

For the difference g(y) between $(t_d - t_p)$ and estimated y

$$g(y) = d/(p - f_c) + (1/a)[1 - e^{-ay}] - y \tag{55}$$

Applying Newton's technique (Burden et al. 1978)

$$y_{n+1} = y_n - g(y_n)/g'(y_n) \tag{56}$$

with

$$g'(y_n) = e^{-ayn} - 1 \tag{57}$$

With the first estimate from Equation 54, y follows from Equations 56 and 57. This method rapidly converges, which gives: $t_d = t_p + y$. With this value for t_d, parameter C in Equation 35 is known. Flow velocity, v, and the Horton constant, a, were

Table 3.2 Types, numbers, and areas of catchments (m^2) used to determine parameter values ω and δ of Runoff-Depth Model (D).

	Type of catchment	No.	Runoff area	Downstream
1	Catchment without weir	1	250	Lined basin
2	Catchment with weir	1	125	Thomson weir
3-10	Micro-catchment with tree	8	116	Basin area 9 m^2

26

determined according to Zarmi et al. (1983) from recession and rising hydrographs, respectively. Depression storage, d, was evaluated from field observations during the start of rainfall-runoff events.

This value of d was checked with the threshold value for runoff, δ, (see Figure 2.9) when runoff depth was plotted against rainfall depth (Boers et al. 1986a). The value of δ varied from 1.9 mm to 3.2 mm, and d was 0.2 mm (Table 3.1). Predicted and measured hydrographs are compared in Figures 3.4 and 3.5. Runoff volumes are shown in Table 3.3, which compares measured volumes with predicted volumes for $d = 0$, Model (A), and for $d > 0$, Model (B).

Measurements to Compare Model (C) with Model (A): Difference between Linear and Non-Linear Recession Curves

The data used were from Experiments 1 and 2 (Table 3.1), with simulated rainfall on a plane of $lxw = 12.50\text{x}10.00$ m^2 by Zarmi et al. (1983). Various m values were used to calculate recession curves: $m = 1$ (linear recession), $m = 3/2$ (from the Chézy Equation; see Equations 16, 17, and 18), $m = 5/3$ (Manning Equation; see Equations 19 and 20), $m = 3$ (Poiseuille Equation; see Equations 21 and 22). For each case, a measured recession curve was used to determine K at the start of the recession and $D(l,0)$ according to Zarmi et al. (1983). For a selected value of m, the corresponding K-value was determined from Equation 44. For the resulting flow-depth relationship, with the use of Equations 45, 51, 42, and 14, the numerical solution was applied to find the recession curve (Appendix A2).

Recession curves were computed at wave-depth steps of $D_0 = 1.0\ 10^{-4}$ m, and for the tail recession, at steps of $D_0 = 0.5\ 10^{-4}$ m. Predicted and measured curves are compared in Figures 3.7 and 3.8 for $m = 1.0$, Model (A), and $m > 1.0$, Model (C). The runoff volume during recession was found by integrating the discharge over recession time, up to t_s, when flow stops. Table 3.4 shows runoff volumes for $m = 1.0$, Model (A), and $m > 1.0$, Model (C).

The flow at the start of the recession was characterized by the Reynolds number: $Re = vD/v$ and the Froude number: $Fr = v/\sqrt{gD}$. The velocity v was calculated from the Chézy Equation (16) with a roughness factor (Equation 17) of $k = 70\ \mu$m, and kinematic viscosity $v(15°C) = 1.14\ 10^{-6}$ m^{2}s^{-1}. The resulting values are shown in Figures 3.7 and 3.8.

Table 3.3. Runoff volumes (10^{-3}m^3) of measured and predicted hydrographs for $t \leq t_e$ with depression storage $d = 0$ and 0.2 mm.

		Area m^2	p mm h^{-1}	t_e min	Meas- ured	$d=0$ mm	$d=0.2$ mm
1	SR	125	59.4	12	800	765	741
2	NR	125	48.0	10	531	515	494
3	SR	125	25.8	12	151	219	189[1]
4	NR	250	10.5	20	191	159	110[2]

SR = Simulated Rainfall, NR = Natural Rainfall
Volume of depression storage [1]$V_d = 25\ 10^{-3}$m^3 [2]$V_d = 50\ 10^{-3}$m^3. (Boers et al. 1994).

27

Table 3.4. Runoff volumes (10^{-3}m^3) from two recession curves measured by Zarmi et al. (1983) on a 125 m^2 catchment area, and from two predicted recession curves with four values of m in Equation 14: m = 1.0, 3/2, 5/3, and 3.0 (Boers et al. 1994).

	p	Measured	Predicted recession curves			
	mm h^{-1}	recession	m = 1.0	m = 3/2	m = 5/3	m = 3.0
1	59.4	157	136	144	144	126
2	37.0	115	87	90	87	72

Measurements to Apply Runoff-Depth Model (D): Determination of Parameters ω and δ

This model was applied to eight micro-catchments with a runoff area of 116 m^2, and a basin area of 9 m^2, each with a tree, and to two catchments without a basin area: one of 125 m^2, and one of 250 m^2. The catchments without a basin area were the same as those used to compare Models (A), (B), and (C), where runoff was recorded with a Thomson weir. Runoff from the 250 m^2 catchment was collected in a 3 m^3 plastic-lined basin, where volumes were calculated from measured water levels. Table 3.2 gives details of all micro-catchments and other catchments.

Each of the eight micro-catchments generated runoff from 116 m^2, which was collected in the basin area of 9 m^2. In each basin area, there was one tree (see Figure 3.2, and Chapter 5 for details of the experimental field). The volume of runoff collected in the basin areas was found from measurements of water depth, b, with a scale on

Figure 3.2 Micro-catchment with runoff area (A is 116 m^2) and tree in basin area (B is 9 m^2). On runoff area in background, the depression storage is visible. The basin is filled with runoff water collected from a desert storm.

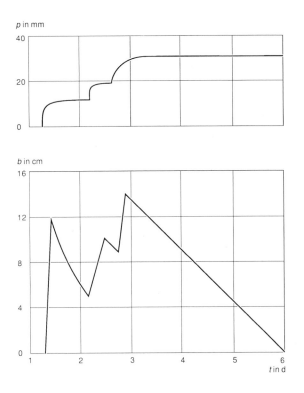

p in mm

b in cm

t in d

Figure 3.3 Illustration of changing water depth b (cm) in basin area of micro-catchment during the period in which storms occurred. The curve shows the depth of water due to rainfall on the basin, inflowing runoff, and infiltration into the rootzone. The upper curve shows cumulative rainfall (Boers et al. 1986b).

a reference level fixed at the bottom. For this measurement, a *storm* was defined, identical to a *24 hour rainfall*, so that storm depth was equal to standard rain-gauge reading. One storm consisted of one or more *showers* during one day (Figure 3.3). To compare rainfall and runoff in volumes, daily rainfall was multiplied by the area.

The volume of runoff water was determined by applying the following equation to each runoff event from each individual shower:

$$V_R = V_B - V_P + V_I \qquad (58)$$

where V_R is the volume of runoff from one runoff event (L^3), V_B is the volume of water in the basin after one runoff event (L^3), V_P is the volume of rainfall on the basin from one shower (L^3), and V_I is the volume of infiltration during one runoff event (L^3).

The volumes of runoff water from each runoff event from each shower were added to complete runoff volume from one storm (one day). For each of the micro-catchments, daily runoff was plotted against daily rainfall, and *linear regression* was applied to determine the threshold value, δ, and the runoff coefficient, ω. The results are presented in Figures 3.9 to 3.11 and Table 3.5.

Table 3.5. Values of runoff coefficient, ω, and threshold value, δ, (mm), obtained by applying the Runoff-Depth Model (D) to n storm runoff events on 10 catchments of A m². The resulting correlation coefficient is r. Linear regression of all storm runoff events on Catchments 3 to 10 yielded the values in the last column.

	1	2	3	4	5	6	7	8	9	10	3-10
A	250	125	116	116	116	116	116	116	116	116	116
ω	.98	.53	.59	.38	.27	.50	.54	.58	.33	.50	.46
δ	2.0	2.1	3.0	3.1	3.6	3.4	3.0	3.2	3.5	3.4	3.2
n	22	20	28	28	28	28	28	28	28	28	224
r	.98	.83	.86	.83	.72	.85	.82	.90	.77	.81	.80

3.2   Comparison of Runoff Prediction

Comparison of Model (B) with Model (A): Effect of Depression Storage on Runoff Volume

Figure 3.4 shows p, $f(t)$, and $q_l(l,t)$, the flow rate per unit area of plane (ms⁻¹) as predicted for $d = 0$ and $d = 0.2$ mm and a comparison with the measured flow in Event 1 from Table 3.1.

The depressions are filled in one minute (shaded area), which causes a delay to the start of runoff. Model (B) approximates the measured curve more closely than

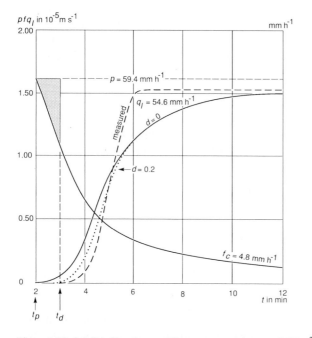

Figure 3.4 Rainfall, infiltration, and flow rate on catchment of 125 m². The $d = 0.2$ mm model approximates the hydrograph more closely than the $d = 0$ solution of Zarmi et al. (1983). Depression storage (shaded area) delays the start of surface flow (Boers et al. 1994).

Model (A) of Zarmi et al. (1983), in which $d = 0$, especially at the start of runoff. Due to the gradual decline in the infiltration rate, the predicted flow rate will reach the plateau later than the measured hydrograph. This causes an underestimate of the predicted runoff volume.

Figure 3.5 shows the measured and predicted discharges for Event 2 (Table 3.1). The depression storage delays the predicted start of runoff from t_p to t_d, so that it is closer to the measured start of runoff. The inclusion of depression storage also shifts the inflection point to a higher position, which is also shown in Figure 3.6. Figure 3.4 shows that the model underestimates runoff volume.

Table 3.3 shows the runoff volumes of four events up to t_e, the time to equilibrium. For comparison, t_e was defined as the time at which the measured and predicted hydrographs had both reached the peak discharge. The data show that agreement between the measured and predicted runoff volumes is best for Events 1 and 2, which have the *highest rainfall rates*. In both events, Model (A) ($d = 0$) predicts a runoff volume lower than the measured volume. The runoff volumes predicted by Model (B) ($d = 0.2$ mm) are even lower. The differences in runoff volumes between Models (A) and (B) equal the depression storage, V_d, of 25 l. The differences between predicted and measured runoff volumes of Events 1 and 2 are low: 4% for Model (A) and 7% for Model (B).

At lower rainfall intensities, agreement is not as good. The prediction for Event 3 is higher than the measured volume. Agreement could be improved by assuming a larger d value, which would increase t_d, delay the start of runoff, and reduce the runoff volume up to t_e. Predictions in Event 4 show the same pattern as Events 1 and 2, but the agreement is less: for Model (A), the runoff volume was underestimated by 17%, and for Model (B) by 42%. The difference between (A) and (B) is the *depression storage* of 50 l on a plane area of 250 m². Agreement between prediction and measurement could be improved by changing the value for a, but the a-values used

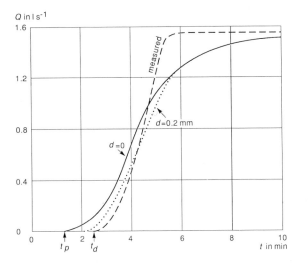

Figure 3.5 Measured and predicted hydrographs of Event 2 (Table 3.1), with depression storage (d is 0.2 mm), and without (d is 0.0) (Boers et al. 1994).

31

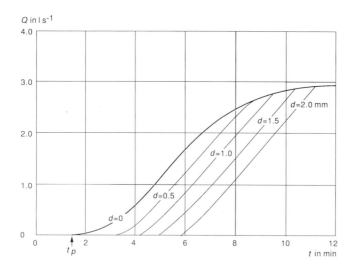

Figure 3.6 Predicted hydrographs from Storm 2 (Table 3.1) on a 250 m² catchment area for various d-values (Boers et al. 1994).

here were those determined by the standard procedure proposed by Zarmi et al. (1983).

Figure 3.6 shows the rising hydrographs produced by Storm 2 from Table 3.1 on a plane of 250 m², for d = 0, 0.5, 1.0, 1.5, and 2.0 mm. Other parameter values are from the same event. For these larger d-values, the hydrograph modification is clearer than in Figure 3.5. For d = 0, $t_p = t_d$ = 1.5 min, and the shape of the hydrograph is the same as for d = 0 in Figure 3.5. For $d > 0$, the start of runoff is delayed and the inflection point on the rising limb shifts to a higher position, where the hydrograph shows a sharp break. This broken shape resembles that of the measured hydrograph in Figure 3.5.

Comparison of Model (C) with Model (A): Effect of Non-Linear Recession on Runoff Volume

Figure 3.7 shows the recession curve measured by Zarmi et al. (1983), following simulated rainfall of p = 59.4 mm h⁻¹ and linear solutions, Model (A), as well as non-linear solutions, Model (C). Qualitatively, Model (C) describes the measured curve better than Model (A). Quantitatively, the *approximation may be improved* by using various m-values. The linear solution approximates the measured curve accurately for $0 < t < 90$ s, but deviates for $t > 90$ s. The non-linear solutions of m = 3/2 and m = 5/3 are similar and are closer to the measured curve than the m = 3 solution; m = 3/2 gives the best approximation.

The measured and predicted runoff volumes for the various solutions are shown in Table 3.4. All solutions underestimate the runoff volume, but with an 8% underestimate, the m = 3/2 and m = 5/3 solutions are the closest to the measured volume.

Figure 3.8 shows the measured and predicted curves as was done in Figure 3.7, but for a lower rainfall intensity: p = 37.0 mm h⁻¹. It is clear that, at a lower flow rate, the approximations are not as good. Only the first section ($t < 45$ s) shows a

32

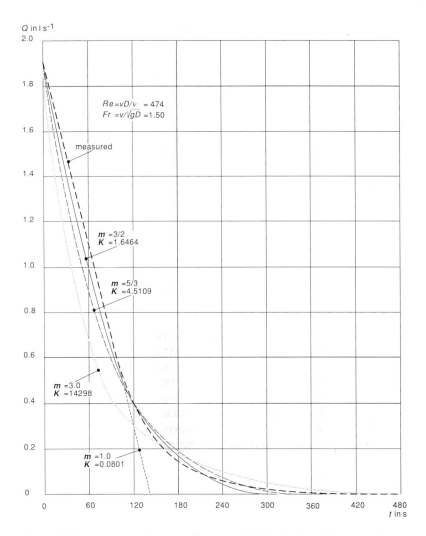

Figure 3.7 Measured recession curve (Zarmi et al. 1983, Exp. 1) and the recession curves predicted with *m* is 1.0, 3/2, 5/3, and 3.0 (Boers et al. 1994).

good prediction by Model (A). The general picture is the same as in Figure 3.7, but the agreement of non-linear solutions is not as good at this lower rainfall intensity. Table 3.4 shows that the **m** = 3/2 solution underestimates the measured volume by a little over 20%.

Application of Runoff-Depth Model (D): Values of Runoff Coefficient ω and Threshold δ

In Figure 3.9, runoff depth is plotted against storm depth for Catchment 1 (Tables 3.2 and 3.5). For 22 events, the correlation coefficient, *r*, was 0.98. Owing to the extreme aridity of this location, the number of events recorded over a period of two rainy seasons is very limited. The runoff was collected in a plastic-lined basin, which

33

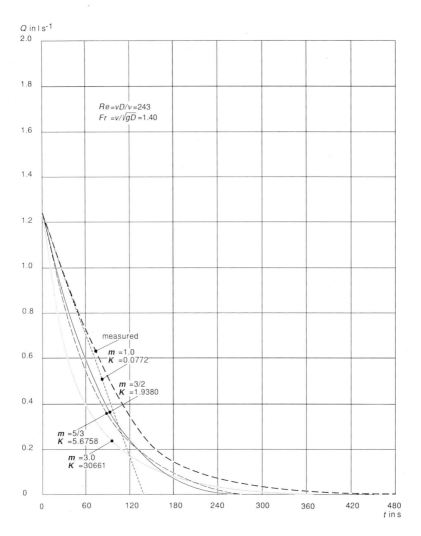

Figure 3.8 Measured recession curve (Zarmi et al. 1983, Exp. 2) and the recession curves predicted with *m* is 1.0, 3/2, 5/3, and 3.0 (Boers et al. 1994).

allowed very accurate measurements. This is reflected in the high correlation coefficient. The runoff coefficient, ω, is 0.98: After the threshold has been satisfied, there is an *almost 1:1 rainfall-to-runoff relationship*. The threshold value, δ, of 2.0 mm is very low because of two factors.

Firstly, raindrop impact has developed a *hard natural surface crust* on the bare soil, which limits infiltration losses. The infiltration rate drops rapidly and time to ponding is short, thereby allowing runoff soon after the start of rainfall. *Secondly*, the smooth and 2% sloping surface has *very little depression storage*. These two factors cause a very efficient runoff generation, almost equal to that on a concrete surface. The model predicts that, once the threshold is satisfied, 98% of the rainfall will be collected as runoff. Some data near the threshold value show storms larger than 2 mm, which

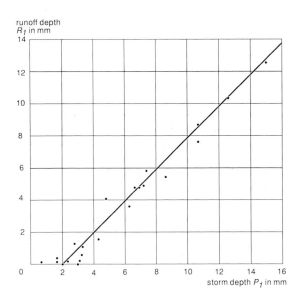

Figure 3.9 Linear regression ($n = 22$, $r = 0.98$) of runoff depth R_1 on storm depth P_1. Parameter values of Model (D) are $\delta = 2.0$ mm and $\omega = 0.98$ for 22 storms on a 250 m^2 catchment area.

give little or no runoff. This is mainly due to low storm intensities, which remain below the infiltration rate.

An interesting aspect for the application of rainwater harvesting is that this is a natural surface which did not require any mechanical treatment. This indicates the potential for runoff generation when topography and soil conditions are favourable. Figure 3.9 is one example, but not all catchments generate runoff so efficiently. Figure 3.10 shows another example, Catchment 2 (Tables 3.2 and 3.5), where 20 runoff events were recorded in two rainy seasons. The spread of data around the curve is larger than for Catchment 1. This results in a lower correlation coefficient of 0.83, which

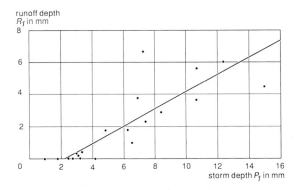

Figure 3.10 Linear regression ($n = 20$, $r = 0.83$) of runoff depth R_1 on storm depth P_1. Parameter values of Model (D) are $\delta = 2.1$ mm and $\omega = 0.53$ for 20 storms on a 125 m^2 catchment area.

35

is partly attributable to less accurate measurements of runoff. Problems of water-level recording in the weir box occurred frequently.

Catchment 2 is only 10 m from Catchment 1 and the micro-topography of the bare surface is similar: smooth, without deep depressions. This is shown in the threshold value of 2.1 mm, almost equal to that of Catchment 1. The difference between them is that the slope of the surface of Catchment 2 is slightly less ($s_0 = 1$ to 2%), and in some spots termite activity in the dry season had disturbed the crust. These factors caused a higher infiltration loss, which explains the lower runoff coefficient of 0.53. The model predicts that, after the threshold value has been satisfied, about 50% of the rainfall will be transformed into runoff. The difference between Catchments 1 and 2 indicates the importance of the effects of *spatial variability in soil conditions*.

Figure 3.11 shows an example of runoff collected in the basin area of a micro-catchment with a tree: Micro-Catchment 8 in Tables 3.2 and 3.5. In two rainy seasons, 28 runoff events were recorded. The correlation coefficient was 0.90. The threshold value was 3.2 mm, somewhat higher than for Catchments 1 and 2, because of some shallow depressions and more infiltration losses than in Catchments 1 and 2. The runoff coefficient of 0.58 is similar to that of Catchment 2. The distance between Catchments 8 and 2 is about 40 m.

One of the problems in an extremely low rainfall zone is that it takes a long time to accumulate runoff data. One approach to reduce this problem is to collect runoff data on different micro-catchments, as was done here. The assumption could then be made that on eight different micro-catchments, one storm produces eight *independent runoff events*. The runoff events are assumed to be independent because of differences in surface conditions of the runoff areas, which determine the *infiltration rate*, *depression storage*, and *slope*.

Under this assumption, 28 storms produce 224 independent runoff events on 8 different micro-catchments. By plotting all 224 runoff depths of Catchments 3 to 10 against the storm depths, and applying linear regression, the parameter values in the last column of Table 3.5 were obtained. The overall average of the runoff coefficient

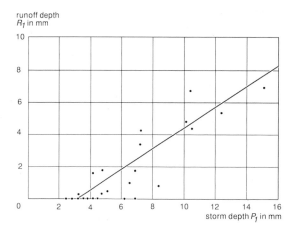

Figure 3.11 Linear regression ($n = 28$, $r = 0.90$) of runoff depth R_j on storm depth P_j. Parameter values of Model (D) are $\delta = 3.2$ mm and $\omega = 0.58$ for 28 storms on a runoff area $A = 116$ m^2 (Boers et al. 1986a).

is 0.46 and the average threshold value is 3.2 mm. The correlation coefficient, r, is 0.80.

Conclusion on the Comparison of Models for Runoff Prediction

Model (B), the kinematic-wave model with depression storage, describes the flow process more realistically than Model (A), which has no depression storage. Model (B) predicts a delayed start of surface flow and a reduced runoff volume. The use of Model (A) would give a more optimistic design: a smaller runoff area. But if runoff prediction is low because of a small runoff area, this cannot easily be changed and will cause failure. *Model (B) gives a more conservative design: a larger runoff area.* If deep percolation then occurs, the groundwater will be recharged.

Model (C), the non-linear recession model, agrees well with the measured recession curves. The best agreement was found for $\boldsymbol{m} = 3/2$ and for a high rainfall intensity. The linear recession of Models (A) and (B) and the non-linear recession of Model (C) both underestimate runoff volumes, but differences between the models are rather small. For micro-catchment design, Model (C) would not add much to the accuracy of runoff prediction as compared with Model (B). The analytical linear solution of *Model (B) is therefore preferred* to the numerical non-linear solution of Model (C).

There was no separate set of rainfall-runoff data available in the Negev Desert to allow the comparison of runoff predicted by Model (D) and by Models (A), (B), and (C). When runoff prediction by Model (D) is being considered, there are two points that need to be discussed.

First of all, the main difference between Model (D) and a kinematic-wave model is that Model (D) does not take *rainfall intensity* into account. In the following two extreme cases, this will cause an error in the runoff predicted by Model (D).

A *low-intensity rain storm* that exceeds the threshold value (e.g. 4 hours of rainfall at 2 mm h^{-1}) will not produce runoff on Catchment 1, but Model (D) would predict almost 6 mm runoff depth from 250 m^2, or roughly 1.5 m^3. On the other hand, a *high-intensity desert storm* that does not exceed the threshold value can produce runoff, whereas Model (D) would predict zero runoff. For example, in a 2-minute burst of 60 mm h^{-1}, the threshold of 2 mm would just be reached. Zero runoff would be predicted, but actual runoff could be almost 0.5 mm or about 0.125 m^3. If Model (D) is applied on a storm basis and predicted runoff is accumulated over a year, the error caused by these extreme cases is small.

The second point of discussion results from the application of Model (D) to *daily rainfall data*, or to standard rain gauge readings. As mentioned earlier, the assumption was made that storm depth equals daily rainfall. The following example shows where this assumption causes the model prediction to deviate from the actual runoff.

If three showers occur on one day, storm depth will be taken as the 24 hour rainfall. Model (D) will apply the threshold concept only once, and predicted runoff may be overestimated. If the three showers were to be recorded separately and each were to be treated as a separate storm, the threshold would be subtracted three times and the model would predict a much lower runoff depth. However, the threshold concept is based on an *initially dry soil* and accounts for the combined loss due to infiltration and depression storage. This means that Model (D) applied to the second and third shower would not be correct, because the infiltration rate is already reduced, and expected runoff would then be underestimated.

The first approach, as followed in this study, *of applying Model (D) on a daily basis is the best*, because for the second and third showers in the above example, the threshold value would be much lower than for the first shower.

Aspects of the practical applicability of Model (D), for which usually only daily rainfall data are available, will be discussed in the next section.

3.3 Comparison of Sheet-Flow-Runoff Models: (A), (B), (C), (D)

The previous sections discussed runoff prediction by Models (A) to (D). In this section, the following aspects of the four models will be compared: (1) *Concept and structure*, (2) *parameters and input requirement*, and (3) *practical applicability*.

Model Concept and Structure
Models (A), (B), and *(C)* are based on concepts with a physical background: kinematic-wave propagation, disturbed sheet flow under raindrop impact, Horton infiltration process, depression storage, and turbulent sheet flow during recession. This physical background yields models with a realistic representation of the relevant process: *flow over an infiltrating surface*. The price of this realism is a relatively complicated model structure.

Model (A) is based on the concept of *sheet flow disturbed by raindrop impact* with $m = 1$, which linearizes Equation 15. Equation 24, subject to conditions (Equation 25), is solved analytically, expressing the model in Equation 26. Runoff starts at ponding time. The S-shaped rising hydrograph is described by Equations 26a and 26b, the plateau by Equation 26c, and linear recession by Equation 26d.

Model (B) is based on the same disturbed flow concept, but the initial condition *includes depression storage*. Equations 15 and 34, subject to conditions (Equation 32), is solved analytically, giving Equations 35a and 35b for the rising hydrograph. The plateau and recession equations (35c and 35d) are identical to those in Model (A).

Model (C) uses the disturbed flow concept of Model (A) up to the end of rainfall, t_r. The rising hydrograph and the plateau are the same as for Model (A). Model (C) assumes that when rainfall stops the *flow regime changes from disturbed to turbulent flow*. The value of m during recession cannot be assumed to equal 1, and Equation 15 is non-linear and is solved with the method of characteristics. This gives a numerical non-linear solution of Equation 15 for the recession curve as Equations 51, 45, and 42.

Model (D) has a concept with less physical background: a *threshold value* for initial infiltration loss and depression storage, and a *runoff coefficient* to take the efficiency of the runoff process into account. This allows a straightforward and robust model structure, which is based on the linear regression of runoff depth on storm depth (Equation 52). The runoff coefficient, ω, transforms potential runoff $(P_I-\delta)$ to actual runoff, R_I. This coefficient, ω, *depends on infiltration in wet soil during runoff*.

Model Parameters and Input Requirement
Model (A) contains five parameters: three for Horton infiltration, f_i, f_c and a (Equation 23), and two kinematic flow parameters m and K (Equation 14). *Model (B)* contains the same five parameters as *Model (A)*, but in Equation 29, there is a sixth parameter,

d, for depression storage, which delays the start of flow. *Model (C)* contains parameters of Model (A), but for the recession equations (Equations 51, 45, and 42), the values of ***m*** and ***K*** are different from those of the rising hydrograph. *Model D* (i.e. Equation 52) has two parameters: ω and δ.

In these sheet-flow-runoff models, (A) to (D), the number and nature of the parameters indicate the *degree of sophistication* and of a realistic representation of the relevant processes. Model (D) is straightforward in producing the runoff depth without describing the flow proces. Models (A), (B), and (C) employ more refined concepts to describe the flow over an infiltrating surface. Defining these concepts mathematically requires more parameters.

Model (A) has parameters that can be determined by analyzing runoff hydrographs from simulated rainfall, as demonstrated by Zarmi et al. (1983). Such experiments are time-consuming and expensive and are not always possible. Alternatively, a portable rainfall simulator (Boers 1990; Boers et al. 1992) can be used to determine the Horton infiltration parameters. For Models (A) and (B), parameter ***m*** is assumed to be 1, and ***K***, which equals v, should be estimated.

Model (B) requires depression storage, *d*, which should be estimated in the field during rainfall. By studying the micro-topography, one can make an estimate of the depression storage. Model (C) is identical to Model (A) during a storm, but employs a concept of turbulent flow after the storm. This requires changing the value of ***m*** for the recession from 1 to 1.5.

Models (A), (B), and (C) differ only slightly in complexity, but it is clear that they are more sophisticated than Model (D). Apart from the parameters discussed above, Models (A), (B), and (C) require as input data: storm depth and storm duration, from which the storm intensity follows. Model (D) requires storm depth only. The selection of a model also depends on its applicability, which will be discussed in the next section.

Practical Applicability for Micro-Catchment Design
For design applicability, it is important to define the *objective of the application*, which in this case is the design of micro-catchments. For this, the first step is *to predict runoff volumes* from recorded series of storms, up to a season or a hydrological year. When applying a model, especially in scarce data zones, it is important to select a model in which one can have confidence. This confidence is a function of model characteristics, methods to determine the parameters and the accuracy of their values, and the quality of the required rainfall records.

Model (D) has a clear structure and its shortcomings were discussed earlier. The model parameters ω and δ are based on concepts that are clear and directly verifiable. The combination of uncomplicated input data (storm depth), only two model parameters, and a very *basic model structure creates confidence in the use of Model (D)*, because the uncertainties involved are limited. Parameter values result from linear regression of storm runoff, and the correlation coefficient indicates how well the model fits the data.

The potential for the application of water harvesting is in arid and semi-arid zones, so the availability of *rainfall records* in those areas is an important factor to consider. In many of these remote areas, the availability of rainfall records is limited to *daily rainfall*, read manually from a Standard Rain Gauge. Recording Rain Gauges, from which storm intensities can be read, are usually found only at weather stations at airports or other meteorological stations.

Model (D) has great applicability in remote areas, provided that the assumption is made that storm depth equals Standard Rain Gauge reading, or that storm depth equals daily depth of rainfall. Daily readings from a Standard Rain Gauge are then used as input data. In many remote areas, runoff data are not available and the values of ω and δ should be estimated in the field. *Soil type and surface crust* indicate the magnitude of infiltration loss during runoff, which determines ω. *Soil type and topography* indicate initial infiltration loss and depression storage expressed in δ.

Model (A) contains more uncertain elements than Model (D) (e.g. the determination of parameter values through hydrograph analysis, infiltration measurements, or other estimates). In addition, Model (A) requires data from a Recording Rain Gauge, which can more easily develop problems than a Standard Rain Gauge, (e.g. mechanical problems in the clockwork, drum rotation, or writing pen). The parameter values and rainfall records required for Model (A) make its applicability limited.

Model (B), when compared with Model (A), has one parameter more, the depression storage, *d*. Otherwise, the models are identical. For design application, depression storage cannot always be ignored and this is the great advantage of Model (B). *Models (A), (B), and (C) are limited in design applicability by available rainfall intensity records*. There is not much difference in the applicability of these three models. In addition to requirements for Model (A), Model (B) needs the field estimate of depression storage, *d*. Model (C) needs the determination of K for $m = 3/2$ during recession, but once K for $m = 1$ is known, this is easy (Appendix A2).

3.4 Final Conclusion on Comparison of Sheet-Flow-Runoff Models

Model (B) is the best to apply in scarce data zones, provided that the required data are available. If they are not available, Model (D) should be used. The main reason for selecting Model (B) is that, for the design of micro-catchments, depression storage, the effect of which is included in the rising limb of Model (B), cannot always be ignored.

4 Theory of Soil-Water-Balance Model SWATRE

4.1 SWATRE General

For the flow below the basin area (Figure 4.1), we can restrict ourselves to vertical flow, as described by Darcy's Law:

$$q = -K(h)[(\partial h/\partial z) + 1] \tag{59}$$

where q is the flux density positive upwards ($L^3L^{-2}T^{-1}$), $K(h)$ is the hydraulic conductivity (LT^{-1}), h is the soil-water pressure head (L), and z is the vertical coordinate, origin at soil surface of basin bottom, *positive upwards* (L).

The change in stored soil water, W, with depth is:

$$\frac{\partial}{\partial z}\left[\frac{\partial W}{\partial t}\right] = \frac{\partial \theta}{\partial t} = \frac{\partial \theta}{\partial h}\frac{\partial h}{\partial t} = C\frac{\partial h}{\partial t} \tag{60}$$

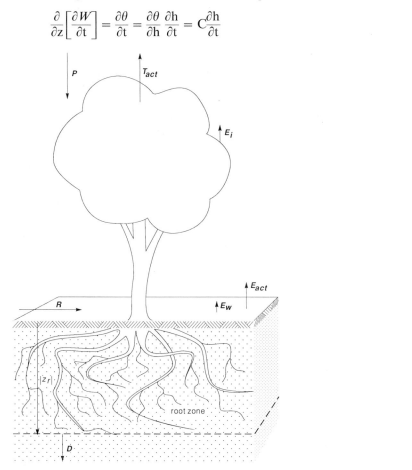

Figure 4.1 Basin area of micro-catchment with a tree and water-balance components as discussed for Equation 1.

where W is the soil water storage in the rootzone (L), θ is the volumetric soil water content (–), $C = d\theta/dh$ is the differential soil-water capacity (L^{-1}), and t is time (T).

The conservation of mass requires that:

$$C[\partial h/\partial t] = -[\partial q/\partial z] - S \tag{61}$$

where S is the volume of water taken up by the roots per unit bulk volume of soil per unit time ($L^3 L^{-3} T^{-1}$).

Combining Equations 59 and 61 yields:

$$\frac{\partial h}{\partial t} = \frac{1}{C(h)} \frac{\partial}{\partial z} \left[K(h) \left(\frac{\partial h}{\partial z} + 1 \right) \right] - \frac{S(h)}{C(h)} \tag{62}$$

S is expressed as:

$$S(h) = \alpha(h) S_{max} \tag{63}$$

where $\alpha(h)$ is a prescribed function of soil-water pressure head (–), and S_{max} is the maximum possible root extraction rate (T^{-1}).

If α equals 1, the transpiration rate is completely controlled by atmospheric conditions; if $0 < \alpha < 1$, the soil-water status becomes important (Figure 4.2). For $h_1 \leq h < h_3$, $S(h)$ is expressed according to Feddes et al. (1978). From h_3 to h_4, $S(h)$ reduces exponentially according to Wesseling et al. (1989)

Equation 62 can be solved numerically. Feddes et al. (1978) and Belmans et al. (1983) developed a *transient 1-D finite difference model SWATRE,* which can be used for a wide range of boundary conditions, when solving problems of saturated or unsaturated flow. To obtain a unique solution of Equation 62, initial and boundary conditions must be specified.

The following discussion of the model theory is split into two separate sections. The application to the extremely arid and arid zones in the Negev Desert is based on the model calibration at an experimental field in Sede Boqer with Pistachio trees, where many measured data were available (see Chapter 5). The application to the semi-arid zones in Niger and Nigeria is based on the model calibration at an experimental Neem windbreak in Sadoré, Niger, for which fewer data were available (see Chapter 7).

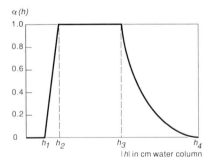

Figure 4.2 Shape of the sink term used to describe the soil-water extraction pattern. Between pressure head h_3 and h_4, the relation is exponential and the value of the exponent is -2 (Wesseling 1989).

For the application of SWATRE to Negev, Niger, and Nigeria, model options were selected that were most applicable to tree characteristics and data availability. Tree characteristics that differ for Pistachio and Neem are root distribution and root water uptake, leaves falling in winter (Pistachio trees), or year-round canopy (Neem is evergreen). Because of data availability, the determination of parameter values and initial and boundary conditions were different. For this reason, the theory will be discussed in *two separate sections*.

4.2   SWATRE Applied to the Negev Desert

The Pistachio trees in the experimental field at Sede Boqer had a rather shallow root system (see Chapter 5). The distribution of root mass and *root water uptake* was assumed to be uniform with depth (Figure 4.3). S_{max} was defined as:

$$S_{max} = T_{max}/|z_r| \tag{64}$$

where T_{max} is the maximum possible transpiration rate (LT^{-1}), and $|z_r|$ is the depth of the rootzone (L).

T_{max} in Equation 64 was calculated from:

$$T_{max} = K_c E_{pan} \tag{65}$$

where K_c is a crop coefficient (–), and E_{pan} is the Class A pan evaporation rate (LT^{-1}).
The *initial condition* is the pressure head as a function of z, specified according to:

$$h(z,0) = h_0 \tag{66}$$

where h_0 is the prescribed pressure head (L).

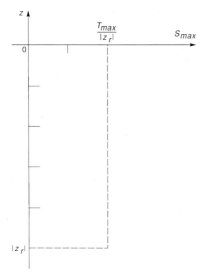

Figure 4.3 Root water uptake pattern assumed constant with depth according to Feddes et al. (1978).

The *lower boundary condition* at the bottom of the soil profile, in the absence of a groundwater table, is described as $\partial h/\partial z = 0$, which means free percolation. For this case, Equation 59 reduces to:

$$q(z=-z_b,t) = -K(h) \tag{67}$$

where $|z_b|$ is the depth of the soil profile (L).

As *upper boundary condition*, a flux density at the surface is used. The flux density through the soil surface $q_s(z=0,t)$, as determined by atmospheric conditions, is calculated as:

$$q_s(z=0,t) = E_s - p_I \tag{68}$$

where p_I is the rain storm intensity (LT^{-1}), i.e. rate of rainfall in one day (cm d^{-1}). For any day in a dry period, the *soil evaporation rate* E_s (LT^{-1}) in Equation 68 was estimated according to Black et al. (1969):

$$E_s = \lambda\sqrt{(t+1)} - \lambda\sqrt{t} \tag{69}$$

With the restriction:

$$E_s < E_{max} = K_e E_{pan} \tag{70}$$

where λ is a soil-dependent parameter (LT$^{-3/2}$), t is the time after the start of a dry period (T) (a dry period ends on the day after which $P > 0.5$ cm d^{-1}), E_{max} is the maximum possible soil evaporation rate (LT^{-1}), and K_e is a soil evaporation factor (–).

The flux density through the soil surface $q(z=0,t)$ is also governed by the transmitting properties of the top soil layer, which can be calculated according to Darcy (Equation 59). During evaporation, the pressure head at the soil surface, h_0, is assumed to be in equilibrium with the surrounding atmosphere. During infiltration, $h_0 = 0$. Actual evaporation/infiltration flux density is taken as the minimum of q_s according to Equation 68, and $q(z=0,t)$ according to Equation 59.

In Equation 68, p_I is the rain storm intensity. Evaporation of *intercepted rainwater* was neglected, since the trees have no leaves during the rainy season, which coincides with the winter. The *open water evaporation* from the basin area during infiltration was also neglected because of the brief period in which it occurs, in the order of a day.

4.3   SWATRE Applied to Niger and Nigeria

The Neem trees in the experimental windbreak at Sadoré, Niger, were assumed to have a root system with shallow horizontally spread roots and a deep tap root. This type of root distribution is often developed in arid environments by trees such as Neem or Eucalyptus. The assumption was made that most of the water is withdrawn from the upper layer, and that *soil-water withdrawal* decreases linearly with depth (Figure 4.4). S_{max} was defined according to Prasad (1988):

$$S_{max}(z) = \frac{2T_{pot}}{|z_r|}\left(1 - \frac{|z|}{|z_r|}\right) \tag{71}$$

where T_{pot} is the potential transpiration rate of the tree (LT^{-1}).

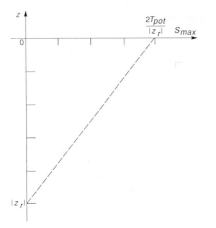

Figure 4.4 Root water uptake pattern, assumed decreasing with depth according to Prasad (1988).

Unlike Sede Boqer, where data were available to relate T_{max} in Equation 64 directly to E_{pan} in Equation 65, data were not available for Sadoré, Niger. Therefore, T_{pot} in Equation 71 was determined as follows:

$$T_{pot} = ET_{pot} - E_{pot} \qquad (72)$$

where ET_{pot} is the potential evapotranspiration rate of the tree (LT^{-1}), and E_{pot} is the potential soil evaporation rate of shaded soil, i.e. bare soil not receiving any radiation under the evergreen closed windbreak canopy (LT^{-1}).

The potential evapotranspiration rate of the tree ET_{pot} was:

$$ET_{pot} = K_{tree}ET_0 \qquad (73)$$

where K_{tree} is the crop factor for the tree (–), and ET_0 is the evapotranspiration rate of a reference crop (LT^{-1}) according to Doorenbos and Pruitt (1977).

The potential soil evaporation rate E_{pot} was calculated as:

$$E_{pot} = K_{soil}ET_0 \qquad (74)$$

where K_{soil} is the soil evaporation factor of bare soil shaded by the windbreak canopy (–).

The evapotranspiration rate of the reference crop ET_0 was found from:

$$ET_0 = K_{pan}E_{pan} \qquad (75)$$

where K_{pan} is the pan evaporation factor (–).

The *initial condition* was defined as:

$$\theta(z,0) = \theta_0 \qquad (76)$$

where θ_0 is the prescribed volumetric soil water content (–).

In the absence of measured θ-values, the θ_0-value was estimated by a procedure described in Chapter 7.

The *lower boundary condition* at the bottom of the soil profile, in the absence of a groundwater table, is free percolation: $\partial h/\partial z = 0$, with Equation 59 reduced to Equation 67.

As *upper boundary condition*, a flux density at the surface was used. The flux density through the soil surface $q_s(z=0,t)$, as determined by atmospheric conditions, was calculated as:

$$q_s(z=0,t) = E_{soil} - p_{l,n} \tag{77}$$

where E_{soil} is the soil evaporation rate under the windbreak canopy (LT^{-1}), and $p_{l,n}$ is the net rainstorm intensity (LT^{-1}), i.e. the rate of rainfall minus water interception in one day (cm d^{-1}).

The soil evaporation rate under the Neem windbreak canopy, E_{soil} in Equation 77, is different from E_s under one Pistachio tree in Equation 68 because of the prevailing conditions. In the Negev desert, rainfall occurs in the winter season, when the *Pistachio trees have no leaves,* and the wet soil in the basin area *is exposed to radiation.* Soil evaporation occurs mainly in this season. During the following growing season, the soil has already dried out in preceding dry spells and, in addition, the tree canopy provides shade to the soil surface.

In Niger, the *Neem trees are evergreen* and the *windbreak canopy is closed.* Rainfall occurs in the summer season, but the *soil is never exposed to direct radiation,* and so the soil evaporation rate in the shade of the windbreak canopy is limited.

At Sede Boqer, data were available to determine the soil evaporation parameter λ in Equation 69, and to relate E_{max} to E_{pan} in Equation 70. These data were not available for Sadoré, and E_{soil} in Equation 77 was assumed to be equal to E_{pot} in Equation 74. This E_{pot} was estimated low by applying a low value of K_{soil}, lower than that given by Doorenbos and Pruitt (1977) for bare field soil exposed to radiation.

The *open water evaporation* from the basin during infiltration was assumed to be negligible for two reasons. First, the infiltration usually takes a relatively short time, and second, in the shade of the canopy, open water evaporation is low.

Evaporation of intercepted rainwater on the leaves of the evergreen Neem windbreak cannot be neglected during summer when evaporation rates are high. Equation 77 takes into account the interception loss in net rainfall rate $p_{l,n}$. In studying the evapotranspiration of a deciduous forest, Hendriks et al. (1990) applied the interception model of Gash (1979), which is based on the approach of Rutter et al. (1971, 1975). In the Rutter approach, weather data on an hourly basis are required, which limits the practical applicability of the model.

Gash (1979) and Mulder (1985) assume three phases in the evaporation of rainwater intercepted by the leaves: (1) *Wetting phase:* the time from the start of the shower to the saturation of the canopy; (2) *Saturation phase:* the time during which the canopy is saturated; (3) *Drying phase:* the time from the end of one shower to the start of the next shower (see Figure 4.5).

Gash (1979) assumes that the evaporation rate and rainfall rate during a shower can be replaced by seasonal averages. The model distinguishes between *small showers,* which do not saturate the canopy, and *large showers,* which do saturate the canopy. The model further assumes that only one shower per day occurs; in other words, that

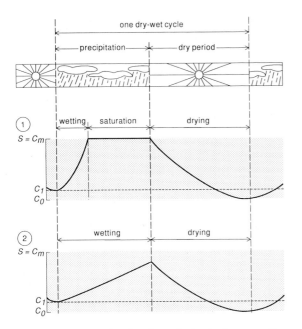

Figure 4.5 Diagram showing change in depth of water on the canopy (C) when saturation is reached (Case 1), or is not reached (Case 2); C_0 is dry canopy, C_1 is partly wet after dry period, C_m is maximum depth of water on the canopy, equal to interception capacity (S) (van Roestel 1984).

the rain depth of a shower equals daily rainfall. The depth of rainfall required to saturate the canopy is calculated as:

$$P_s = -(C_s p_{av}/E_{av}) \ln [1-(E_{av}/p_{av})/(1-f)] \qquad (78)$$

where P_s is the depth of rainfall required to saturate the canopy (L), C_s is the canopy storage capacity (L), p_{av} is the seasonal average rainfall intensity (LT^{-1}), E_{av} is the seasonal average evaporation rate of wet canopy during rainfall (LT^{-1}), and f is the free throughfall coefficient (–).

For *large storms*, the interception, E_i, is calculated per phase:

1) Wetting phase: $E_i = P_s(1-f) - C_s$ (79)

2) Saturation phase: $E_i = (E_{av}/p_{av})(P_r - P_s)$ (80)

3) Drying phase: $E_i = C_s$ (81)

For *small storms:*

1) Wetting phase only: $E_i = P_s(1-f)$ (82)

5   Calibration of SWATRE at Sede Boqer, Negev Desert

5.1   Experimental Set-Up for Data Collection

The data used are from an experimental field with trees at Sede Boqer in the Northern Negev Desert, Israel, which is situated on a plain in the Negev Highlands region. The Negev Highlands consist of rolling loess plains separated by numerous low hills composed mainly of limestone. The altitude is 200 to 400 m above mean sea level. The average annual temperature is 19 to 20 °C (Dan et al. 1973).

The climate is *extremely arid*. Mean annual rainfall is 90 mm, with extreme values of 34 mm and 167 mm (Yair and Danin 1980). Rainfall is limited to the winter season, which extends from October to April. The rainy season is followed by a dry growing season from April to October. The soil in the area is *clay loam of aeolean origin*, which was deposited as a loess cover, several metres thick, on a limestone bedrock. Textural differences in a horizontal direction are small. In a vertical direction, there is a tendency towards somewhat lighter texture with increasing depth. Average dry bulk density ρ_d from 0 to 0.50 m is 1.45 g cm^{-3}.

The experimental field was used (a) to determine water-balance components: rainfall, surface runoff, soil-water storage, soil evaporation, and transpiration, which can be used for model calibration, and (b) to measure the required parameters for the models: infiltration characteristic, depression storage, surface flow velocity, hydraulic conductivity, and the soil-water retention characteristic.

The experimental field (Figure 5.1) consists of two *catchments* (1 and 2, Table 3.2) of 250 m^2 and 125 m^2, respectively, without basin areas, eight *micro-catchments* with a tree (Catchments 3 to 10, Table 3.2) of 125 m^2 each (runoff area $A = 116$ m^2 and basin area $B = 9$ m^2) and ten *control basins* of 9 m^2 with one tree each. Runoff from Catchment 1 was collected in a plastic-lined basin. At the downstream end of Catchment 2, flow rates were measured with a Thomson weir and a recorder. The surface of the catchments is bare, crusted, and smooth, without deep depressions, sloping 1 to 2% (Figure 5.2).

The borders of Catchments 1 and 2 and Micro-Catchments 3 to 10 were 0.15 m high plywood strips. Vegetation and rocks had been removed from all runoff areas. Each basin area located at the downstream end of a micro-catchment had one Pistachio tree (*Pistacia vera L.*) of the Kerman cultivar. Similarly, each control basin had one Pistachio tree, and received rain directly falling on the basin, but no runoff water (Figures 5.3 and 5.4).

A rainfall simulator in the field was used for the experimental work required for model development, and to supplement rain and runoff water to the trees in case a drought year occurred (Figure 5.5). The sprinklers were spaced 4 m apart in a triangular pattern. The nozzles were mounted on 3 m high risers and sprayed 2 to 3 m upwards, so that the drops had a *free fall of 5 to 6 m*. For Catchment 2 (Figure 5.1), where surface flow was measured, the sprinklers were mounted on cables stretched over the field. To limit the cost of the simulator for the entire field, risers were used instead of cables (see Figures 5.3 and 5.4).

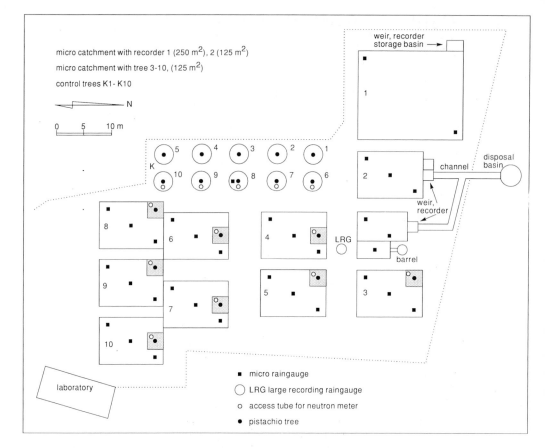

Figure 5.1 Layout of the experimental field of the Institute for Desert Research in Sede Boqer. At the northern side, two catchments (1-2) with weirs and recorders for flow measurements. On the eastern and southern side, eight micro-catchments (3-10), each with a runoff area A of 116 m², basin area B of 9 m², and tree in the basin. On the western side, ten control trees (K1-K10) in basins which do not receive runoff water.

In the basin area of each of the eight micro-catchments with trees, and in five of the ten control basins with trees, access tubes for neutron gauge measurements were installed. The tubes extended 0.25 m above the basin bottom to prevent the entry of flood water, and reached a depth of 1.80 m. For the calibration of SWATRE, the data of two micro-catchments (4 and 8) and two control basins (7 and 9) were used. The water balance components in the micro-catchments and control basins were measured during the hydrological year 1982/83. Data from the rainy season 1983/84 were used for verification.

During the *rainy season,* runoff is available, but the trees are dormant, have no leaves, and thus transpiration is negligible compared with soil evaporation. During the *growing season,* rainfall and runoff are negligible, while transpiration is significant compared with soil evaporation. The two seasons can therefore be characterized as

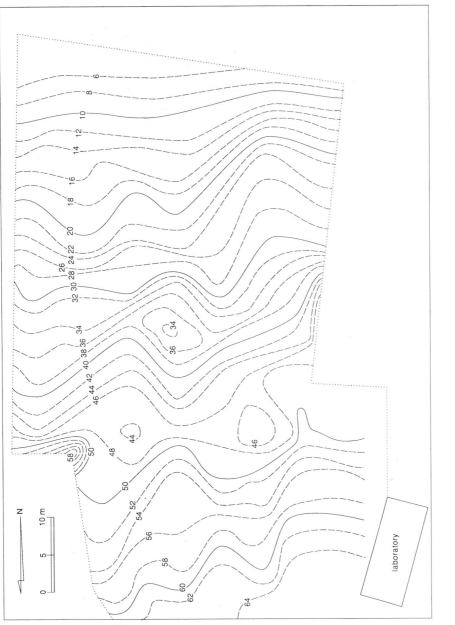

Figure 5.2 Contour map (cm) of the experimental field (Figure 5.1). Surface slope in the area varies from 1 to 2%.

51

Figure 5.3 Southern side of the experimental field immediately after a runoff event. The basin areas of micro-catchments contain rainfall and runoff water, whereas the control basin in the foreground contains rain water only. Runoff areas show little storage in shallow depressions. During the winter season, Pistachio trees are dormant and without leaves (Boers et al. 1986b).

Figure 5.4 The surface of a runoff area dries out during a dry spell after a storm period. Dark spots indicate shallow depressions where more water infiltrated. A few days later, the dark spots have disappeared (Boers et al. 1986b).

Figure 5.5 Layout of a rainfall simulator on the experimental field, covering one catchment (2) on the northern side for flow measurements, eight micro-catchments with trees (3-10) on the eastern and southern side, and ten control trees in basins (K1-K10) on the western side.

53

(quantities are defined below Equation 1):

Rainy season, 1 October – 1 April: $E_{act} > 0, T_{act} = 0, I > 0$ (83a)
Growing season, 1 April – 1 October: $E_{act} = 0, T_{act} > 0, I = 0$ (83b)

For calculations, 1 October was defined as Day 1.

5.2   Hydrological and Soil Physical Measurements

Meteorological data were collected from a station of the Institute for Desert Research, 100 m from the site. Rainfall was measured with a standard rain gauge, which was read every morning at 09.00 h, and a recording rain gauge. A Class A pan was used to measure the daily open water evaporation rate, E_{pan}. The calculation of evaporation losses from the ponded water in the basins during the infiltration process showed that these losses were small compared with soil evaporation losses and were therefore neglected.

The maximum possible transpiration rate of the trees, T_{max}, in Equation 65 was estimated from an experiment with two Pistachio trees in two control basins (6 and 10; see Figures 5.6a and 5.6b). The trees were irrigated twice a week and, after each irrigation, the soil surface was covered with plastic to prevent soil evaporation. Every other night, the plastic was removed to allow aeration of the rootzone. The transpiration was then derived from the change in soil-water storage. Quantities of irrigation water to replenish the rootzone were kept small enough to prevent deep percolation losses. Values of K_c in Equation 65 were computed from the ratio of measured values for T_{max} and E_{pan}. A value of $K_c = 0.60$ was found.

The value of the soil-dependent parameter λ in Equation 69 was calculated by plotting E_s, measured with an infra-red thermometer, against $\sqrt{t}$. For the winter season, this was found to be $\lambda = 0.80$, and for the summer season $\lambda = 0.35$. The value of the soil evaporation factor in Equation 70 was calculated to be $K_e = 0.65$.

Surface flow rates from Catchment 2 at the northern side of the experimental field were monitored and used for model development (Chapter 3). At the downstream end of each catchment, runoff was collected in a gutter and channelled through a weirbox and over a 90° triangular Thomson weir (see Figure 5.7). The water level in front of the weir was measured with a float connected to a recorder. The weir was calibrated on the site. Volumes of runoff followed from the integration of the hydrographs.

Hydrographs of surface runoff were measured from natural desert storms and from simulated rainfall. Rainfall simulations were performed during the night, when pressure in the supply system was highest and wind speed was lowest. All simulations with constant rainfall intensity were continued until equilibrium conditions had been reached. When rainfall was being simulated, the depth and uniformity of application were checked by placing 30 cm high tube-gauges on the surface and calculating the Christiansen coefficient of uniformity (Israelsen and Hansen 1962).

The volume of runoff water, V_R, collected in the basin areas of micro-catchments with trees was found from Equation 58, as was discussed earlier. Soil-water storage below 0.25 m was calculated from weekly neutron-gauge measurements at depth

Figure 5.6a Two Pistachio trees in control basins were selected to determine the water requirement of these trees. During the growing season, the trees received water twice a week to keep the soil near field capacity. Once a week, the soil-water content in the profile was measured with a neutron gauge, and soil water was subsequently replenished. Measurements of soil-water content extended to 1.75 m depth to check and prevent deep percolation loss.

Figure 5.6b After each application – when infiltration was completed – the basin was covered with a plastic sheet to prevent evaporation. In this way, the maximum potential annual transpiration T_{max} of the tree was estimated.

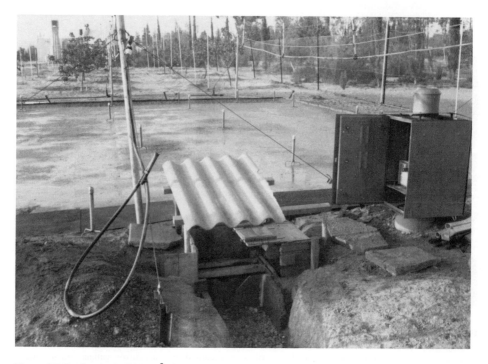

Figure 5.7 Catchment 2 of 125 m^2 after an experiment with a rainfall simulator suspended over the area. Runoff over natural desert pavement was measured with a Thomson weir and a water-level recorder. Drying surface shows low depression storage.

increments of 0.10 m. The bottom of the soil profile was taken at a depth of 1.70 m, because neutron-gauge measurements could not be taken deeper. During the installation of the access tubes, the dry bulk density was measured from core rings and the soil-water content of each 0.10 m layer was measured gravimetrically. These data were used to calibrate the neutron gauge. Figure 5.8 shows an example of some soil-water-content profiles.

Soil-water storage in the top layer (0 to 0.25 m), where the neutron gauge could not be used, was measured gravimetrically with one repetition. *Average rooting depth* of 1.00 m was found from an inspection of the excavated root systems of two trees, from observations during the installation of neutron-gauge access tubes, and from weekly profiles of soil-water content during root water uptake.

The trees had been planted in 1973 and had been trickle-irrigated with a minimum application to survive. The water-holding capacity of the loess soil is quite good, so that depth of infiltration was very limited. Under conditions of low rainfall, low irrigation, and shallow infiltration, roots remained shallow and rooting depth was assumed constant at 1.00 m.

Soil-water retention curves were determined in the laboratory from undisturbed core samples taken from the profile below each basin at depths of 0.40 m and 0.80 m, with one repetition (see Figure 5.9a). The saturated hydraulic conductivity of undisturbed core samples was measured in a constant head permeameter described

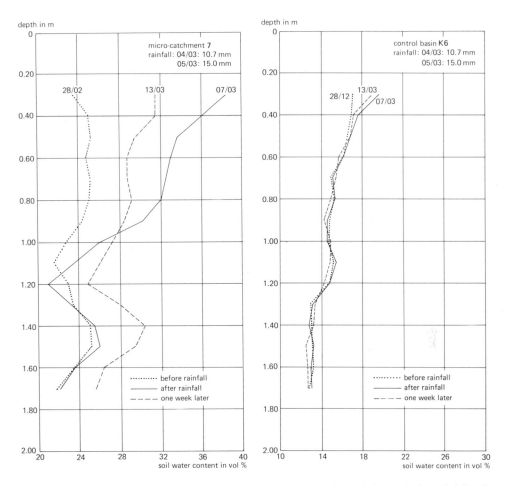

Figure 5.8 Soil-water profiles of Micro-Catchment 7 and Control Basin K6 before and after rainfall and one week later. Rainfall on 4 March (10.7 mm) and on 5 March (15.0 mm) produced runoff on Micro-Catchment 7 and caused a significant increase in soil-water content. One week later, a portion of the water had percolated to the subsoil. Rainfall on Control Basin K6 caused only a slight increase in soil-water content at 30 cm depth. Soil water in the top layer of 30 cm can easily reach the surface and evaporate, in contrast with soil water stored in deeper layers.

by Wit (1967). The *unsaturated hydraulic conductivity* was determined from field measurements of soil-water content, taking into account Darcian flux density according to the approach described by Feddes (1971; Table 2), and from soil-texture data according to Bloemen (1980) and Wesseling et al. (1984) (see Figure 5.9b).

5.3   Model Calibration on Data from Sede Boqer, Negev Desert

SWATRE was used to predict soil-water storage, W, and the predicted results were compared with the measured values of soil-water storage for the hydrological year

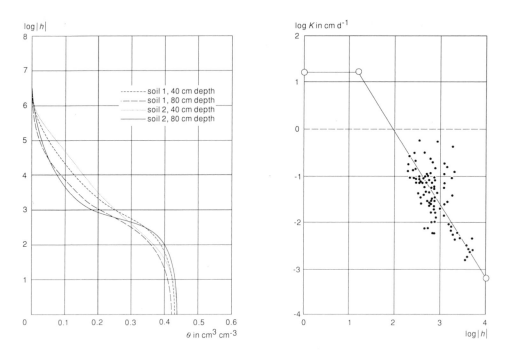

Figure 5.9a Soil-water retention curves of Soil 1 and Soil 2 for two depths, as used in SWATRE.
Figure 5.9b Unsaturated hydraulic conductivity as a function of soil-water suction. The points indicate values calculated according to Feddes (1971, Table 2). The line indicates the relationship calculated from soil-texture data according to Bloemen (1980) and Wesseling et al. (1984) for Soils 1 and 2 (Boers et al. 1986a).

1982/83. Disagreement was found, especially after a heavy storm, when a large volume of runoff water infiltrated. Differences were mainly caused by *lateral soil-water flow*, not accounted for in the 1-D model.

The actual wetted soil volume below the basin has an ellipsoid shape, which may be assumed to be between a sphere and a cylinder. For a sphere, the wetted volume increases with the third power of the radius; for a cylinder with the second power of the radius. In both cases, the model was sensitive to this correction. By taking into account the shape of the wetted area, a correction could be applied by assuming that the horizontal cross-section of the wetted soil volume below the basin B^* was 11 m^2, instead of the basin area B of 3 x 3 m^2, measured at the highest water level over which surface water intake occurred (Figure 5.10).

The results of the calibration for Catchment 4 are presented – as an example – in Figure 5.11, which shows that the general trend of the predicted storage values agreed well with the measured values throughout the year. The absolute soil-water storage computed by the model was within 10% of the measured values. The model is therefore *capable of describing the soil-water balance*.

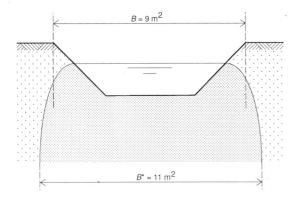

Figure 5.10 Diagram of basin area (B is 9 m^2) in which water infiltrates into the soil. For the calibration of the model, a horizontal cross-section through the wetted soil mass below the basin B^* of 11 m^2 was assumed, to account for some lateral flow (Boers et al. 1986a).

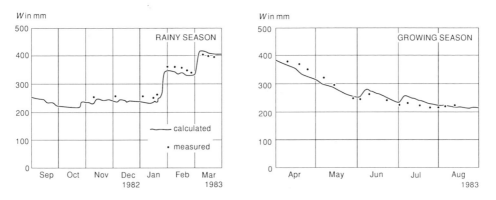

Figure 5.11 Measured and predicted values of soil-water storage for the hydrological year 1982/83 at Sede Boqer (Boers et al. 1986a).

5.4   Combination of Runoff-Depth Model with SWATRE

Predictions for micro-catchment design were made with the calibrated SWATRE model at Sede Boqer (extremely arid zone) and at Beersheva (arid zone). For selected average, dry, and wet years at these two locations, only records of daily depth of rainfall were available. For this reason, the runoff was predicted with a *runoff-depth model (Model D)* from Chapters 2 and 3. These micro-catchment design predictions will be discussed in Chapter 6. For design predictions with SWATRE and runoff models in Niger and Nigeria, see Chapters 8 and 9.

6 Prediction of Micro-Catchment Design for Extremely Arid and Arid Zones

6.1 Selected Climate and Soil for Prediction of Micro-Catchment Design

For the micro-catchment design prediction, the rainfall data from Sede Boqer were taken as an example of an *extremely arid zone* (average annual rainfall 90 mm), and from Beersheva as an example of an *arid zone* (average annual rainfall 200 mm). Table 6.1 shows the soil properties of Micro-Catchments 4 and 8, as well as the actual annual rainfall of the years that were used in the prediction for each of the climatic zones.

Prediction runs were made for the twelve combinations indicated in Table 6.1, and for various sizes of runoff area and basin area. For each of these combinations, a control run, simulating a control basin without runoff, was included. In a control run, R was put at zero, so that total infiltration, I, was equal to P in Equation 2, because both E_w and E_i were neglected in the extremely arid and arid zones.

The discussion is restricted to the results of the *average years,* with some additional comments about dry and wet years. The distribution of the annual rainfall over individual storms is important from the viewpoint of runoff generation, and thus for the whole rainwater-harvesting process. Storms smaller than the threshold value, δ, in Equation 52 produce no runoff at all. Larger storms, however, provide significant volumes of runoff. In spite of this, the *total annual rainfall, P,* was used as a general indicator for climatic zones, under the assumption that increased annual depth of rainfall should increase with the number of storms exceeding the threshold value.

Each tree in a micro-catchment in the experimental field is considered an isolated tree, as the distance between these trees varies from 10 to 20 m. Because the required basin area for isolated trees is not known, the water balance of the basin area was calculated in units of volume (m³). For a fixed basin area, as in the designed windbreak in Chapters 7, 8, and 9, the water balance of the basin can be calculated in units of

Table 6.1 Selected combinations (+) of climatic conditions (extremely arid zone) and soil properties (Micro-Catchments 8 and 4 with soil types 1 and 2 resp.) for the design predictions.

Soil properties			1	2
Runoff coefficient ω			0.58	0.38
Threshold value δ (mm)			3.2	3.1
Hydraulic conductivity			$K(h)$	$K(h)$
Soil water retention curve			$h(\theta)$	$h(\theta)$
Climatic zones	Year		Rainfall (mm)	
Extremely arid zone	77/78	dry	51	+	+
Average annual	78/79	average	75	+	+
rainfall: ca.90 mm	79/80	wet	158	+	+
Arid zone	78/79	dry	124	+	+
Average annual	79/80	wet	339	+	+
rainfall: ca. 200 mm	80/81	average	217	+	+

depth (mm). For water balance calculations in volumes, Equations 2, 3, and 4 become (neglecting E_i and E_w):

$$I* = P* + R* \tag{2a}$$

$$L* = E_{act}* + D* \tag{3a}$$

$$T_{act}* = I* - L* \tag{4a}$$

where the * indicates an expression in dimensions of volume (L^3):
$P*$ is $PB*$, $R*$ is $RB*$, $E_{act}*$ is $E_{act}B*$, and $D*$ is $DB*$. Whereas B is the basin area at maximum water level, $B*$ is the horizontal cross-section of wetted soil below the basin (Figure 5.10).

From data of Spiegel-Roy et al. (1977) on yield as a function of annual quantity of harvested water, it has been concluded that for Pistachio trees an annual volume of 7 to 10 m³ of water should be available for actual transpiration in order to obtain a good yield (see Figure 6.1). For the design predictions, we used Equation 4a as design equation, and took $T_{act}*$ equal to 7 m³ *as design target*.

6.2 Prediction of Micro-Catchment Design for Extremely Arid and Arid Zones

(1) *First prediction series*. The results of the first prediction for a micro-catchment size of 125 m² (i.e. runoff area is 116 m² and basin area is 9 m²) are shown in Table 6.2. The second-last column shows $T_{act}*$ for a tree with catchment. For comparison, $T_{act}*$ of a tree without micro-catchment has been added in parenthesis in the last column. Although the micro-catchment increases transpiration significantly, $T_{act}*$ is

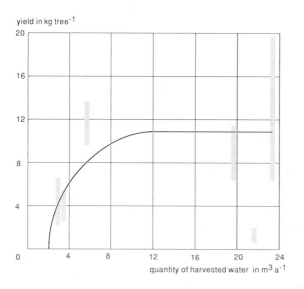

Figure 6.1 Yield of Pistachio tree, Kerman cultivar, as a function of total annual infiltration $I*$ (i.e. volume of harvested rainwater) (Boers et al. 1986a).

Table 6.2 Annual water balance terms from Equation 1 ($E_i = E_w = \Delta W = 0$), calculated in m^3 for average years in two climatic zones, two soil types, and with catchment area 125 m^2 (runoff area A = 116 m^2, basin area B = 9 m^2)

Climatic zone	Annual rainfall	Soil type	Rainfall P^*	Runoff R^*	Soil evapora-tion E_{act}^*	Deep percola-tion D^*	Transpir-ation T_{act^*}	Control T_{act}^*
Extremely	75 mm	1	0.7	2.3	1.1	0.3	1.6	(0)
arid zone	75 mm	2	0.7	1.5	1.1	0.1	1.0	(0)
Arid zone	217 mm	1	2.1	10.5	1.4	7.7	3.5	(0.7)
	217 mm	2	2.1	6.9	1.4	5.2	2.4	(0.7)

very low in all four cases. Table 6.2 further shows that an important quantity of water is supplied by the runoff, and that evaporation and deep percolation losses occur.

In the *extremely arid zone,* the total annual infiltration, I^*, is very low, and roughly half of it is used for transpiration. A larger runoff area would be required to produce the volume of infiltration needed to cover the water requirement. The surface of Micro-Catchment 8, with Soil 1, is more efficient in producing runoff than the surface of Micro-Catchment 4, which results in 50% more actual transpiration. The two soil conditions do not differ in actual soil evaporation. Deep percolation is negligible.

In the *arid zone,* the same micro-catchments would produce four times as much infiltration in an average year, which would more than double T_{act}^*. Evaporation would not increase significantly. On the other hand, deep percolation would increase sharply, which shows that the storage capacity of the rootzone below a basin of 9 m^2 would be too small. From these data, we can draw two conclusions: (a) in the extremely arid zone, a *larger runoff area* is required to increase total infiltration, to allow for more actual transpiration; and (b) in both zones, more storage capacity in the rootzone is required – which means a *larger basin area* – for more actual transpiration.

(2) Second prediction series. In the following prediction runs, the water balance was predicted under a set of different design specifications. The same climatic zones and soil properties applied. Two parameters were varied: runoff area and basin area. First, the catchment area for each climatic zone was kept constant, at 250 m^2 for the extremely arid zone and at 125 m^2 for the arid zone, while the basin area was varied. The results for an average year are shown in Figure 6.2.

Figure 6.2a shows the results for Soil 1 in the arid zone. For comparison, the actual transpiration $T_{act}^*(2)$ of Soil 2 has been added. I^* increases with larger B, but at the same time L^* increases. T_{act}^* reaches 7 m^3 for B is 40 m^2, which satisfies the design criterion. This size of basin corresponds with the traditional 6 x 6 m^2 planting pattern of trees in irrigated orchards, which means that one tree has about 36 m^2 for horizontal root expansion. At B is 40 m^2, $T_{act}^*(2)$ would reach almost 6 m^3, which would give a yield below the target. The bottom curve shows that in the *extremely arid zone* a catchment area of 250 m^2 still does not bring actual transpiration to an acceptable level.

In Figure 6.2b, the terms I^* and L^* from Figure 6.2a are analyzed. If B increases, the volume of rainfall on the basin increases. Since, at the same time, the runoff area

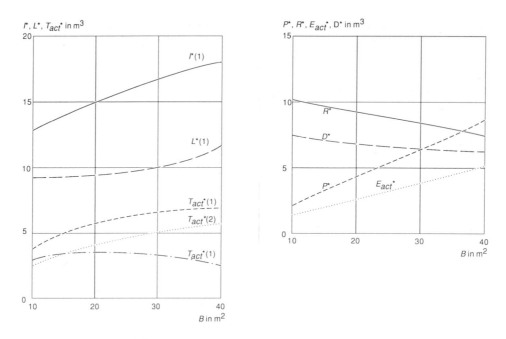

Figure 6.2a Total annual infiltration $I^*(1)$, losses $L^*(1)$, and transpiration $T_{act}^*(1)$, as a function of basin size B with catchment area 125 m² in Soil 1. The data simulate an average year (1980/81) in the arid zone with an annual rainfall of 217 mm. For comparison, transpiration for Soil 2: $T_{act}^*(2)$ has been added. The bottom curve $T_{act}^*(1)^*$ indicates transpiration in the extremely arid zone with a catchment area of 250 m².

Figure 6.2b Total annual rainfall P^*, runoff R^*, soil evaporation E_{act}^*, and deep percolation D^*, as a function of basin size B with a catchment area of 125 m². The data simulate an average year (1980/81) in the arid zone with P is 217 mm. (This is the case presented in the three top curves in Figure 6.2a; Boers et al. 1986a).

becomes smaller, runoff decreases. In the transformation of rainfall to runoff in Equation 52, water is lost, which means that the decrease in runoff to the basin is smaller than the increase in rainfall on the basin. The result is that the sum of both curves increases with the basin area. Figure 6.2b shows that deep percolation decreases with an increasing basin area, because storage capacity increases. At the same time, the evaporating surface of the basin becomes larger, so that E_{act}^* increases. The result is that the sum L^* increases (Figure 6.2a). For Soil 2, the same trends were observed (not shown here).

From the results discussed above, the following conclusions can be drawn: (a) for the arid zone and with the trees considered, the *basin area should be approximately 40 m²;* and (b) a *micro-catchment of 250 m² is too small* for the extremely arid zone and, for such dry areas, rainwater harvesting from micro-catchments with natural surfaces is not the appropriate technology.

(3) *Third prediction series.* In this series of prediction runs for the arid zone, the basin area was kept constant at 40 m², and the following values were used for A: 40, 80,

64

120 and 160 m². Figure 6.3a shows the results for Soil 1 in an average year. By increasing A, both I^* and L^* increase. Increasing A from 40 m² to 80 m² gives a slight increase in T_{act}^*, which is close to the potential transpiration. A further increase of A results – in an average year – in increasing losses L^*.

Figure 6.3b shows the results of a dry year (1978/79: P is 124 mm) with all the other conditions the same. For a dry year, a larger runoff area would increase T_{act}^* significantly. L^* would increase only slightly. For A is 80 m², T_{act}^* would be 3.5 m³ in a dry year. For the same A in a wet year (not shown here), the actual transpiration would be about the same as for the average year (Figure 6.3a), but L^* would be very much larger.

From the results discussed above, the following conclusion can be drawn: for the arid zone, the most suitable *runoff area is between 40 m² and 80 m²*.

The approach described above is suitable in arriving at a *preliminary design*. For a detailed design, more specific criteria should be developed, taking into account variability in rainfall, efficiency of water use, and the relationship between yield prediction and available water. That, however, is beyond the scope of this study. The losses discussed above indicate that the water is not used efficiently. This aspect can be expressed with the concept of water-use efficiency:

$$e_u = T_{act}^*/I^* = T_{act}/I \tag{84}$$

where e_u is the water-use efficiency (–).

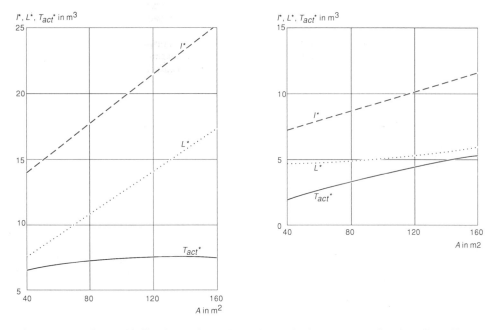

Figure 6.3a Total annual infiltration I^*, losses L^*, and transpiration T_{act}^*, as a function of runoff area A, with basin size B is 40 m², for an average year (1980/81) in the arid zone (P is 217 mm).
Figure 6.3b Total annual infiltration I^*, transpiration T_{act}^*, and losses L^*, as a function of runoff area A for a dry year (1978/79) in the arid zone (P is 124 mm) (Boers et al. 1986a).

65

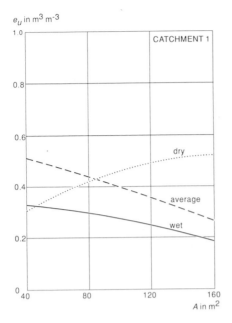

Figure 6.4 Water-use efficiency e_U as a function of runoff area A, with basin area B is 40 m² for a dry year (1978/79: 124 mm), an average year (1980/81: 217 mm), and a wet year (1979/80: 339 mm) in the arid zone (Boers et al. 1986a).

Figure 6.4 shows e_u in dry, average, and wet years as a function of A. The general picture is that, *as conditions become drier, the water is used more efficiently*. In an average year, e_u drops from 0.58 to 0.46, when A increases from 40 m² to 80 m². For the same increase of A in a dry year, the value of e_u would increase from 0.32 to 0.44. In wet years, increasing A from 40 m² to 80 m² would lower e_u from 0.34 to 0.30.

Application to Yield Prediction
On the basis of the available data, the following observations can be made on yield prediction. Figures 6.5 and 6.6 express the use of land and water, respectively, for yield prediction of the Kerman cultivar. Figure 6.5 shows the yield in kg/tree as a function of A. In an average or wet year, a runoff area larger than 40 m² leaves the yield practically constant. In a dry year, the yield increases significantly when A goes from 40 to 80 m² and beyond that. For A is 60 m² in an average year, the yield would be 5 kg/tree. The micro-catchment area for one tree would be 100 m², so that the yield would amount to 500 kg/ha.

Figure 6.6 shows the predicted yield relative to the use of water (i.e. per m³ total infiltration I^*) as a function of A. The trends are similar to those observed in Figure 6.5. For average and wet years, the relative yield decreases, but in a dry year, and when A goes from 40 m² to 80 m², it increases significantly. For A is 60 m², the yield in average and dry years would be close to 0.6 kg per m³ infiltrated water. These observations support earlier conclusions about the required runoff area.

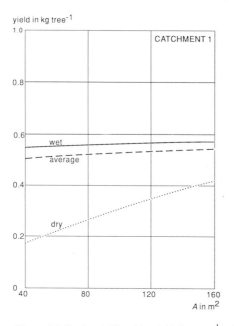

Figure 6.5 Predicted Pistachio yield (kg tree^{-1}) of the Kerman cultivar, as a function of runoff area A, with basin area B is 40 m^2 for a dry year (1978/79: 124 mm), an average year (1980/81: 217 mm), and a wet year (1979/80: 339 mm) in the arid zone (Boers et al. 1986a).

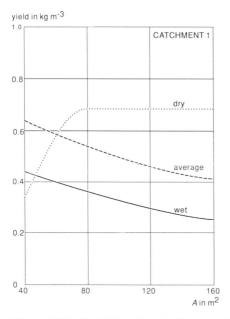

Figure 6.6 Predicted Pistachio yield, Kerman cultivar, per m^3 of total infiltration $I*$ (kg m^{-3} water) as a function of runoff area A, with basin area B is 40 m^2 for a dry year (1978/79: 124 mm), an average year (1980/81: 217 mm), and a wet year (1979/80: 339 mm) in the arid zone (Boers et al. 1986a).

67

6.3   Conclusion on Micro-Catchment Design in the Negev Desert

Two aspects make the design discussed above specific. The trees are not closely spaced, but are isolated, and, without leaves, they cannot shade the basin area during the rainy season. Besides, rainfall and runoff occur in the same season, and root-water uptake and transpiration occur in another season. This requires a large W_{max} to carry the stored soil water from one season to the next. The loess soil has a good water-holding capacity, $\theta_{FC}-\theta_{WP}$, but $|z_r|$ is only 1 m, so that a large B is required. A large basin area, exposed to radiation, means *high soil evaporation,* which is enhanced by capillary rise to the surface. Small $|z_r|$ means deep percolation starts below 1 m.

The combination of the above-mentioned factors has led to the finding that the extremely arid zone is too dry for micro-catchments and requires larger catchments. For the arid zone, with a basin area of 40 m², the runoff area should be between 40 m² and 80 m². So, for the arid zone, prospects for the application of micro-catchments look good. An important factor that affects the design is the *type of tree and its rooting depth.* For another type of tree with larger $|z_r|$, storage in depth increases, and B can decrease, which reduces $E_{act}*$ and $D*$.

7 Calibration of SWATRE on a Neem Windbreak in a Semi-Arid Zone at Sadoré, Niger

7.1 Windbreaks and Neem Characteristics for SWATRE Application

Arid and semi-arid lands cover approximately one-third of the land surface of the world, and have about 600 million inhabitants (Gregory 1984). A large area in Africa falls within this category. In the arid environments of the deserts, only isolated spots with a scarce water supply offer limited scope for human settlement. In large areas of West Africa, one crucial problem is water. The scarcity of water, because of the uncertainty of rainfall, presents a major obstacle to the rational development of agriculture (Sivakumar et al. 1979).

The Sudano-Sahelian semi-arid zone of West Africa has a harsh climate, with low and highly variable rainfall, high soil and air temperatures, high evaporative demand, and poor soils. The production of adequate and renewable supplies of food and firewood in this zone is severely limited by the scarcity of water. The need for fuel forces an increasing number of people to collect wood from larger areas. This deforestation leads to desertification in the Sudano-Sahelian zone (United Nations 1977).

The establishment of trees in areas where natural forests do not grow has been used in arid and semi-arid regions as a means of alleviating harsh weather conditions. In particular, *shelterbelts and windbreaks* have been used to protect humans, livestock, and crops against the ravages of wind (Ujah and Adeoye 1984). The major limiting factor to tree establishment and growth in the semi-arid zones is *shortage of water*. Consequently, the major requirements are to promote soil-water conservation through weed control, mulching, and soil preparation, and to promote early deep root growth through good soil preparation and proper management of the available water (Ritchie 1988).

A *windbreak* generally consists of a double row of trees planted around the boundary of a farm on the windward side. Windbreaks are usually 150 m long and contain 100 trees each. They are primarily designed to reduce wind erosion, while small quantities of forest produce will also become available when the trees mature. The windbreak model is popular with farmers, as it takes up very little space and also serves to demarcate their farm boundary (Hedeselskabet 1990).

Windbreaks are recommended and used for soil conservation and crop protection over much of dryland Africa. Extensive lines of windbreaks have been established in many areas of the Sahel. One example in northern Nigeria is the Katsina Afforestation Project, funded by the Nigerian Government and the European Union. Windbreaks increase crop yields in their lee, decrease soil erosion, and produce wood for fuel and construction (Ujah and Adeoye 1984; Bognetteau-Verlinden 1980; Long and Persaud 1988).

For windbreaks and shelterbelts, the Neem tree is recommended and is extensively used in the Sudano-Sahelian zone (Benge 1988; Brenner et al. 1991; FAO 1974; National Academy of Sciences 1980; Radwanski 1980; Madougou et al. 1987; van

Latum 1985). Available information on biomass production and water use in agroforestry systems is very limited. The few studies conducted on this subject refer mainly to humid areas. Windbreak and shelterbelt design is still mainly based on practical experience.

Neem Characteristics
In the application of SWATRE to the semi-arid conditions of Niger and northern Nigeria, this study deals with Neem only, and in particular with *Neem trees in windbreaks*. The main reason for this is that an experimental Neem windbreak at Sadoré, Niger (Brenner et al. 1991), established at the Sahelian Centre of the Institute for Crops Research in Semi-Arid Tropics/ICRISAT, was used to calibrate SWATRE.

Neem is native to India, Pakistan, Sri Lanka, Malaysia, Thailand, and Burma. The tree was introduced into northern Nigeria in 1928 and is now widely cultivated on the African continent, particularly in rainfall-deficient regions. *Neem is evergreen*, although it loses part of its leaves in the dry season. The Neem tree takes 10 to 15 years to become fully grown, at a height between 12 to 18 m (Benge 1988). Branches are spread widely and form an oval crown. Leaves are about 22 to 32 cm long, are composed of 7 to 17 leaflets, and are about 6 to 7 cm long (Ketkar 1976). The tree flowers in the later part of the dry season (Fishwick 1970).

Neem seems to grow best in deep sandy soils that are well drained, but it can grow in practically all types of soil. Growth is not good on poorly drained soils, because the taproot then tends to rot and the tree gradually dies. Experiments in the Sudan zone of Nigeria have shown that the initial height growth and the individual stem diameters are markedly reduced at closer spacings: for spacings of 0.9 m x 0.9 m and 5.5 m x 5.5 m, heights were 2.0 m and 3.8 m, respectively (De Jussieu 1963).

The water relationships of windbreaks (*tree hydrological characteristics*) in the semi-arid tropics, particularly for soil depths exceeding the crop rooting zone, are not known (van den Beldt 1989). The unsaturated zone in the Majija Valley site, Niger, is 7 to 10 m deep, which is probably thinner than the Neem rooting zone. In tropical and southern hemisphere areas, plantings of evergreen trees and shrub species predominate in shelterbelts, and tend to exclude grasses and ground flora once canopy closure has been achieved (Ritchie 1988).

Application of SWATRE to Neem Windbreak
In view of the water shortage described above, SWATRE was applied to predict T_{act} of a Neem tree in a windbreak for two cases: (1) a tree in a basin area with *rainfall only* and no runoff, and (2) the same tree in a micro-catchment with *rainfall and runoff*. For the calibration of SWATRE, this chapter deals with Case (1) only. Chapters 8 and 9 deal with Case (2), where SWATRE is applied for micro-catchment design predictions. For model calibration, data from a windbreak were used at Sadoré (13°15′N; 2°17′E), the experimental farm of the ICRISAT Sahelian Center, located 45 km south of Niamey.

A soil survey of this area was conducted by West et al. (1984). The soils are sandy, and the rainfall and temperature pattern (Niamey average 29 °C) is typical of the Sahel, which supports a vegetation of grasses and thorny bushes with scattered trees, such as *Acacia albida*. Geomorphologically, the area has gently sloping plateaus with

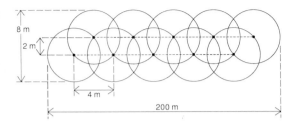

Figure 7.1 Layout of an experimental windbreak at ICRISAT Sahelian Centre, Sadoré (Brenner et al. 1991), used for model calibration.

discontinuous sand covers and broad sand plains. The experimental windbreak is located on Dayobu sand (Brenner et al. 1991).

Dayobu sand is a very deep soil, gently sloping (0 to 2%), which occurs in concave positions. Typically, these soils are yellowish-red sands throughout the profile and have weak structural development. The surface horizon is normally about 29 cm thick with 7 to 10 cm of more-recently deposited overburden. The Bt-horizon extends to about 175 cm in most areas, with a C-horizon extending to depths greater than 2 m. Depth to laterite gravel is about 2 to 4 m (West et al. 1984). The profile at the windbreak location (Brenner et al. 1991) was taken as *3 m Dayobu sand on laterite gravel*.

The windbreak (Figure 7.1) consisted of a double row of six-year-old Neem (*Azadirachta indica A. Juss.*), planted 4 m apart in 2 m wide rows in a triangular planting pattern. The total number of trees was 100. If micro-catchments were to be used, this would give each tree a minimum basin area, B, of 8 m². The average height of the windbreak was about 6 m (Brenner et al. 1991).

The trees developed a closed windbreak canopy. The assumption was made that, under *natural rainfall conditions,* crown and root development of these trees was such that a projection on the soil surface would cover 16 m². The windbreak was 196 m long and effectively 8 m wide, covering nearly 1600 m² of soil and providing about 1200 m² of vertical windbreak surface.

The hydrological year in the area consists of two distinct seasons, which are characterized by the quantities from Equation 1 as:

Rainy season, 1 May – 1 October: $I > 0, T_{act} > 0, E_{act} > 0$ (85a)
Dry season, 1 October – 1 May: $I = 0, T_{act} > 0, E_{act} > 0$ (85b)

Calculations with SWATRE were done for complete hydrological years from 1 May to 30 April, with 1 May taken as Day 1. The rainy season ends on 30 September, which is Day 153.

7.2   Hydrological and Soil Physical Data

Rainfall and Evaporation
Records of daily rainfall, P_l, and daily evaporation, E_{pan}, measured with a standard rain gauge and a Class A pan from 1982 to 1989 were available from the ICRISAT Sahelian Centre at Sadoré (Hoogmoed 1991). Table 7.1 summarizes the input data

Table 7.1. Data required to predict T_{act} of Neem in windbreaks as described in Section 7.2 for experimental windbreak Sadoré, Niger

Type of data	Parameters	Table
1) Daily rainfall and evaporation:	P_l, E_{pan}	
2) Root water uptake function, $\alpha(h)$:	h_1, h_2, h_3, h_4	Table 7.2
3) Maximum soil-water withdrawal, S_{max}:	T_{pot}, $|z_r|$	
4) Factors for ET_0, ET_{pot}, E_{pot}, T_{pot}:	K_{pan}, K_{tree}, K_{soil}	Table 7.3
5) Initial soil-water content:	θ_0	
6) Evaporation of intercepted rain, E_i:	p_{av}/E_{av}, C_s, f	Table 7.4
7) Soil hydraulic parameters:	$K(\theta)$, $h(\theta)$	

Table 7.2. Soil-water pressure head values (cm water), decreasingly negative, defining starting points of uptake sections in the soil-water withdrawal function as given in Figure 4.2 (Feddes et al. 1978).

Start uptake	Optimal uptake	Reduced uptake	End uptake
$h1 = -5$ cm	$h2 = -10$ cm	$h3 = -600$ cm	$h4 = -16,000$ cm

Table 7.3. Values of factors K_{pan}, K_{soil}, and K_{tree} in Equations 75, 74, and 73 to calculate ET_0, E_{pot}, and ET_{pot} of Neem trees in a windbreak at Sadoré, Niger (after Doorenbos and Pruitt 1977)

Factor	May	Jun	Jul	Aug	Sep	Oct	Nov	Dec	Jan	Feb	Mar	Apr
K_{pan}	.70	.70	.75	.75	.75	.65	.65	.65	.65	.65	.65	.65
K_{soil}	.15	.15	.15	.15	.15	.15	.15	.15	.15	.15	.15	.15
K_{tree}	.70	.65	.65	.65	.65	.70	.70	.70	.75	.75	.70	.70

and refers to parameter values for the application of SWATRE, which will be discussed below.

Soil-Water Withdrawal
Soil-water withdrawal, defined in Equation 63, was calculated with values of soil-water pressure head, h, in the α-function given in Table 7.2. S_{max} was calculated with Equation 71, while T_{pot}, ET_{pot}, E_{pot}, and ET_0 were determined from Equations 72, 73, 74 and 75. The values of K_{tree}, K_{soil}, and K_{pan}, estimated according to Doorenbos and Pruitt (1977), are given in Table 7.3.

Initial Condition: Soil-Water Content, θ_0
In the absence of measured θ-values, the initial soil-water content θ_0, which defines the initial condition in Equation 76, was determined by trial and error as follows. The assumption was made that, on an annual basis, ΔW equals zero. This assumption is based on the fact that the rainy season is followed by a long dry season, in which the roots will take up all available soil water.

For a selected value of θ_0, initial soil-water storage, W_0, was known and SWATRE calculated the final soil-water storage W_f, at the end of the hydrological year. If the increase $\Delta W = W_f - W_0$ was not zero, a new θ_0 value was selected, W_f was re-calculated, and ΔW was re-checked. The procedure was repeated until a θ_0-value that gave

$\Delta W = 0$ was found, and this θ_0 was used as the initial condition. In the sandy soils, θ_0-values varied from 2 to 3%.

Lower Boundary Condition: Free Percolation
The absence of a groundwater table (see Chapter 4) allows, as a lower boundary, the condition $\partial h / \partial z = 0$, for which Equation 59 reduces to Equation 67.

Upper Boundary Condition: Flux Density at Soil Surface
The upper boundary condition was described by Equation 77. Because of continuous shade from the windbreak canopy, the evaporation rate of the soil under the windbreak is low. After the rainy season, the soil surface dries out completely, which reduces E_{act} to nil. As discussed in Chapter 4, E_{soil} was assumed equal to E_{pot} in Equation 74. The value of K_{soil} in Equation 74 was set at 0.15 throughout the year.

Evaporation Rate of Intercepted Rainwater
In Equation 77, the evaporation rate of intercepted rainwater was determined from Equations 78 to 82. Values for the ratio of p_{av}/E_{av} were calculated per month, and varied between about 50 in August to 18 in March. Average rainfall intensity, p_{av}, was calculated with data available from Niamey Airport (Hoogmoed 1991). The average evaporation rate of wet canopy during rainfall, E_{av}, was not known and the data of the average monthly potential evapotranspiration at Niamey Airport were therefore applied instead (Verhoef and Feddes 1991).

For the canopy storage capacity, C_s in Equation 78, no data were available and the following estimate was made. Neem has leaves composed of 7 to 17 leaflets. Each leaflet is 6 to 8 cm long and 1 to 3 cm wide. Average surface area per leaflet is 7 x 2 = 14 cm². The surface area of an average leaf, a_l, composed of 11 leaflets, is 11 x 14 cm², or about 150 cm². An average Neem tree in the experimental windbreak has a total leaf area, A_l, of roughly 30 m² (Brenner et al. 1991). Two extreme cases were considered: (a) a tree with a large number of small leaves, and (b) a tree with a small number of large leaves.
(a) *A small leaf* composed of 7 leaflets, each 6 x 1 cm², gives a total $a_l = 42$ cm². The total number of leaves per tree is 30/0.0042 = 7143. If the average drop diameter is assumed to be 3 mm, its volume is 14.1372 10^{-9} m³. If, on each leaf, one drop were to be retained, then one tree would retain: 7143 x 14.1 10^{-9} m³ = 0.101 10^{-3} m³, which, projected on the soil surface area of 16 m², would mean 0.0063 mm. If 20 drops are retained on each leaf, then $C_s = 0.125$ mm.
(b) *A large leaf* composed of 17 leaflets, each 8 x 3 cm², or total $a_l = 408$ cm². The total number of leaves per tree is 30/0.0408 = 735. If the average drop diamater is assumed to be 3 mm, its volume is 14.1372 10^{-9} m³. If, on each leaf, one drop were to be retained, then one tree would retain: 735 x 14.1 10^{-9} m³ = 0.010 10^{-3} m³, which, projected on the soil surface, would mean 0.0006 mm. If 200 drops are retained per leaf, then $C_s = 0.130$ mm.

Based on the above estimate, $C_s = 0.125$ mm was used in Equation 78. Since the windbreak had developed a closed canopy, a value of $f = 0$ was applied for the free throughfall coefficient in Equation 78. Table 7.4 gives a summary of the parameter values used.

Table 7.4. Parameter values to determine evaporation of rainwater intercepted by Neem canopy according to Gash model (Equations 78-82)

Parameter	C_s (mm)	f	p_{av}/E_{av}
Value	0.125	0	50 (August) – 18 (March)

Evaporation of Open Water
Evaporation loss from ponded water in the basin area, E_w, was considered negligible compared with soil evaporation losses, because of the short period of ponding and the shading by the Neem canopy.

Rooting Depth
The depth of the rootzone, $z = |z_r|$, was estimated as follows. The assumption was made that root depth is a function of infiltration depth. This assumption was based on the fact that, in a dry climate, root growth is governed by the search for water, and that roots cannot and will not grow into deep dry layers.

Shallow infiltration in a dry year will result in shallow rooting depth. In an average year, infiltration will be deeper, the roots will follow the water, and rooting depth will be deeper. In a wet year, infiltration and rooting depth will be even deeper. If a dry year follows, the roots will probably die back to a shallower depth. Based on these considerations, *rooting depth is assumed equal to infiltration depth.*

This depth of infiltration below the basin was found by calculating deep percolation for an average year at an increasing rooting depth. When the maximum rooting depth is found, below which the model calculates negligible deep percolation in an average year for these conditions, this depth is assumed to be the rooting depth. Calculation of T_{act} was performed with this rooting depth for selected average, wet, and dry years.

Soil Hydraulic Functions $K(\theta)$ and $h(\theta)$
A complete description of the soil hydraulic functions, $K(\theta)$ and $h(\theta)$, was not available. Data on soil texture and $h(\theta)$ were compared with standard soils of the Staring Series (Wösten et al. 1987). It was decided that $h(\theta)$ of Dayobu sand was best represented by a *very fine to moderately fine sand* with a median grain size of between 105 μm and 210 μm, and less than 3% organic matter (Staring Subsoil O1). For the subsoil, a *coarse sand* with a median grain size of between 210 μm and 2000 μm with 0-3 % OM was selected (Staring Subsoil O5). The soil hydraulic functions of these two standard soils were used in the calculations for the top layer of 3 m and for the subsoil, respectively (Figure 7.2 a, b).

7.3   Model Calibration on Data from Sadoré, Niger

The calibration of SWATRE was done by calculating T_{act} with the model and comparing these values with the T_{act}-values which followed from the sap fluxes measured by Brenner et al. (1991) on specific dates in the period September 1989 to March 1990. The unknown quantity in the calibration was the *rooting depth* $|z_r|$ in Equation 71 of Prasad (1988), which was adjusted to bring calculated and measured T_{act}-values into agreement.

74

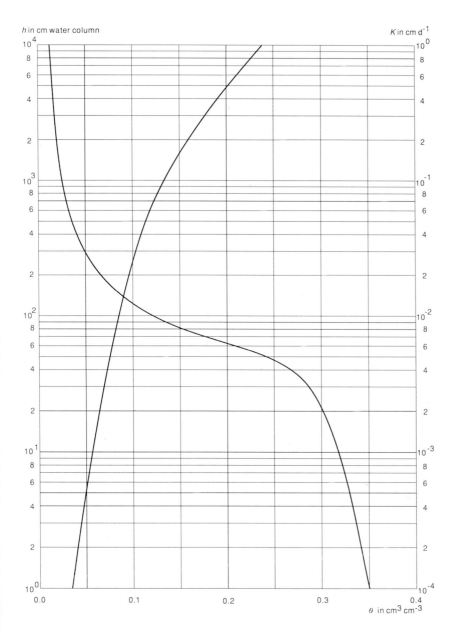

h in cm water column   K in cm d^{-1}

θ in cm^3 cm^{-3}

Figure 7.2a Soil hydraulic functions $K(\theta)$ and $h(\theta)$ of very fine to moderately fine sand, Standard Soil O1 of the Staring Series (Wösten et al.1987), assumed to represent Dayobu sand hydraulic parameters for calibration.

Table 7.5 shows the results of the calibration. The top line shows the specific sampling days when sap flux was measured (Brenner et al. 1991). The second line shows the calculated values of T_{pot}. The following lines show the calculated values

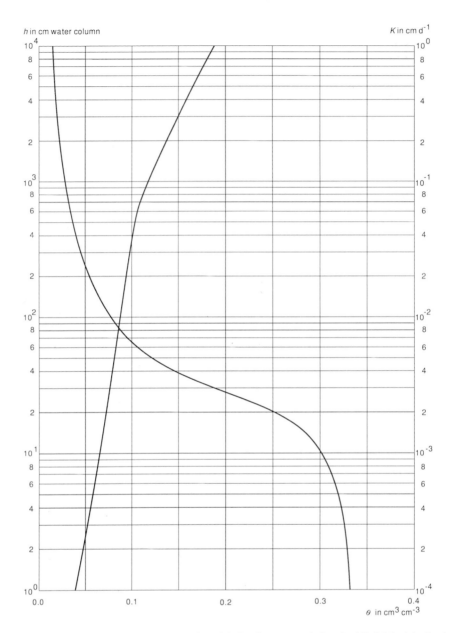

h in cm water column

K in cm d^{-1}

θ in cm^3 cm^{-3}

Figure 7.2b Soil hydraulic functions $K(\theta)$ and $h(\theta)$ of coarse sand, Standard Soil O5 of the Staring Series (Wösten et al.1987), assumed to represent subsoil hydraulic parameters for calibration.

of T_{act} for rooting depths $|z_r|$ equal to 3, 3.5, 4, and 4.5 m (first column). The bottom line shows four values of T_{act}, which are the averages of measurements taken in four periods, on Days 182-196, 209-223, 258-279, and 312-318. In all calculations, the *top 3 m of the rootzone consisted of Dayobu sand,* while at larger rooting depths the *lower*

Table 7.5. Calculated T_{pot} and T_{act} (mm d^{-1}) of Neem on given day numbers at increasing root depths $|z_r|$ of 3, 3.5, 4, and 4.5 m, and T_{act} as determined from average sap fluxes measured in four periods on Neem windbreak at Sadoré, Niger (Brenner et al. 1991)

					Day number						
	182	196	209	213	223	258	263	269	279	312	318
				Calculated potential transpiration rate, T_{pot}							
	2.9	3.8	4.2	3.5	3.9	2.7	3.9	2.8	4.5	6.4	5.3
				SWATRE calculated actual transpiration rate, T_{act}							
$|z_r|$											
3	2.3	3.0	3.2	2.6	2.8	1.7	2.4	1.7	2.4	0.0	0.0
3.5	2.2	3.0	3.3	2.6	2.9	1.8	2.6	1.8	2.6	2.0	1.3
4	2.1	2.9	3.3	2.7	2.9	1.9	2.7	1.9	3.0	2.9	1.2
4.5	1.8	2.4	2.8	2.3	2.6	1.8	2.5	1.8	2.7	2.8	2.2
				Average measured actual transpiration rate (mm d^{-1})							
		3.0			3.3			2.5			2.8

layer was laterite gravel of 0.5, 1, 1.5 and 2 m thickness, respectively.

Starting at 3 m rooting depth, from Day 182, the calculated T_{act} reached values close to the measured T_{act}. On Days 209 and 263, calculated and measured values of T_{act} were almost equal. From Day 312, T_{act} became zero due to lack of soil water. Therefore $|z_r|$ was increased to 3.5 m, and transpiration then existed up to Day 318. On Day 312, calculated T_{act} was 2.0 mm d^{-1}, while measured T_{act} was 2.8 mm d^{-1}. On the next line, rooting depth is 4 m and actual transpiration then amounts to a rate comparable to the measured rate.

At 4.5 m rooting depth, on Days 263 and 312, T_{act} was 2.5 and 2.8 mm d^{-1}, respectively, which is equal to the measured values. At the same time, on Days 182, 196, and 209, calculated T_{act} became 1.8, 2.4, and 2.8 mm d^{-1}, respectively. So the agreement seems less than for 4 m rooting depth. *At 4 m rooting depth, agreement between measured and calculated T_{act} is closest.*

Evaluating this rooting depth by comparing it with actually observed rooting depth in the area was not possible, since none of these trees had been excavated. Experience from the region, however, has shown that a 4 m rooting depth for these trees is very well possible (Hoogmoed 1991). In the search for water under the prevailing circumstances, Neem trees are capable of developing even deeper rooting systems.

The importance of the data in Table 7.5 is not to see whether calculated and measured values are equal on the 11 sampled days. The important point is that there is *reasonable agreement between calculated and measured values.* From this agreement, it was concluded that the model is capable of predicting T_{act} adequately for the design of micro-catchments in this study.

Figure 7.3 shows T_{act} as calculated by SWATRE for the rooting depth of 4 m and as determined from sap flux measurements. At the start of the rainy season on 1 May

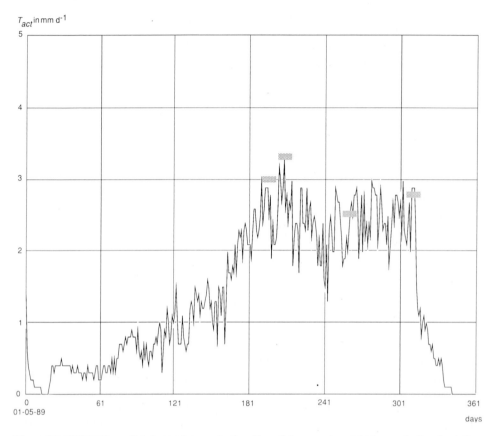

Figure 7.3 SWATRE predicted actual transpiration T_{act} of the experimental Neem windbreak at the ICRISAT Sahelian Centre, Sadoré, Niger. Actual transpiration T_{act} determined from measured sap flux on sample days is indicated in four blocks.

1989 (Day 1), T_{act} was low and gradually increased. On 1 October (Day 153), the dry season started. The four horizontal bars indicate values of measured T_{act} on sampled days. Figure 7.3 shows general agreement between measured and calculated values as discussed in Table 7.5.

78

8   Comparing Prediction of Runoff by Kinematic-Wave Model (B) and Runoff-Depth Model (D) for Micro-Catchment Design with SWATRE

8.1   Runoff Prediction by Models (B) and (D) at Niamey

From Niamey Airport, located 45 km northwest of Sadoré (see Chapter 9), storm intensity data were available for a period of 13 hydrological years, from 1970 to 1983. The data from 1979 are missing. During this period, 370 storms were recorded (Hoogmoed 1991). These data allowed the application of the Kinematic-Wave Model (B). The runoff prediction could be compared with that of the Runoff-Depth Model (D) by routing all storms through both models. Table 8.1 shows the 13 years of annual rainfall at Niamey.

The purpose of this section is to predict runoff with both models and to check which parameter values can be assumed to give a *reasonable runoff prediction*. In the present study, this comparison can only be made with Niamey storm data. The upper half of Table 8.2 shows the five parameters of the Kinematic-Wave Model (B) and the values that have been applied. The values of the infiltration parameters, f_i, f_c, and a, were derived from data of Hoogmoed (1981), measured on crust-forming sandy soils in Mali (see Figure 8.1).

Values for flow velocity, v, were not available at Niamey. It was assumed that, for short distances of sheet flow over gentle slopes under rainfall, this value would be similar to the first two values in Table 3.1, so v is 0.080 ms^{-1} was taken. Various values for depression storage, d, were tried. The lower half of Table 8.2 shows the values for parameters of the Runoff-Depth Model (D) that were applied. On the basis of

Table 8.1 Annual rainfall, **P**, (in mm) for 13 Hydrological Years, HY, (1 May to 30 April) from 1970/71 to 1983/84, at *Niamey, Niger*. The average over these 13 years was 459 mm.

HY	70/	71/	72/	73/	74/	75/	76/	77/	78/	80/	81/	82/	83/
P	482	455	**236**	382	**466**	**668**	563	577	532	392	464	319	430

Table 8.2 Parameter values used to predict runoff by Kinematic Wave Model (B), with Parameter Sets (1) and (2): f_i, f_c, a, v, d_1, d_2, and d_3, and by Runoff Depth Model (D), with δ and ω, at Niamey, Niger.

Set	f_i $(10^{-5}\,\mathrm{ms}^{-1})$	f_c $(10^{-5}\,\mathrm{ms}^{-1})$	a (s^{-1})	v (ms^{-1})	d_1 $(10^{-3}\,\mathrm{m})$	d_2 $(10^{-3}\,\mathrm{m})$	d_3 $(10^{-3}\,\mathrm{m})$
(1)	1.82	0.28	0.0096	0.08	0.0	0.1	0.25
(2)	0.99	0.27	0.0106	0.08	0.0	0.1	0.25
$\delta(10^{-3}\,\mathrm{m})$:	4.0	5.0	5.5	5.75	6.0	6.25	6.5
ω:	0.25						

79

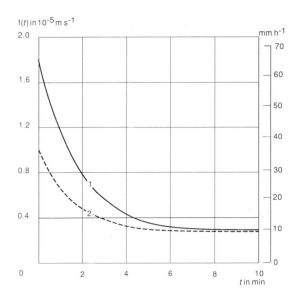

$f(t)$ in 10^{-5} m s^{-1}

Figure 8.1 Infiltration curves of crust-forming sandy soils in Mali, derived from measurements of Hoogmoed (1981). Typical for crust-controlled infiltration is the fast drop in the rate, which then reaches the final constant value in a short time.

field experience, the threshold values, δ, were not estimated too low, and *realistic values* were assumed. The runoff coefficient, ω, was estimated at 0.25. A value of 0.30 was also tried, but seemed too optimistic under non-experimental conditions.

Table 8.3 show runoff volumes accumulated over 13 years of storms as predicted by the Runoff-Depth Model (D) for different threshold values, δ, from a 20 m^2 runoff area. The runoff coefficient, ω, was kept at 0.25. As δ increases, *predicted runoff decreases.* When δ increases from 4 to 5 mm, the runoff volume decreases by 1.466 m^3. When δ increases further from 5 to 6 mm, the runoff volume decreases by a further 1.355 m^3.

When the Kinematic-Wave Model (B) is being applied, the infiltration characteristic is important. Table 8.4 shows the effect of the *infiltration parameters* from Table 8.2 on the predicted runoff volume. Infiltration Characteristic (2) has a lower f_i-value and a higher a-value, which causes the infiltration rate to drop more rapidly than for Infiltration Characteristic (1). Over the 13-year period, this adds up to a difference of 0.945 m^3. For the predictions in this study, it was decided to use Infiltration Characteristic (2).

Table 8.3 Accumulated runoff volumes, R_{ac}, from a runoff area of 20 m^2, predicted by Runoff Depth Model (D) for the years 1970-1983, at various threshold values, δ, with a runoff coefficient, ω, of 0.25.

	Threshold value δ (mm)						
	4.00	5.00	5.50	5.75	6.00	6.25	6.50
R_{ac} (m^3)	22.882	21.416	20.729	20.395	20.061	19.744	19.425

80

Table 8.4 Accumulated runoff volumes, R_{ac}, from a runoff area of 20 m², predicted by Kinematic Wave Model (B) for the years 1970-1983, with two different infiltration characteristics from Parameter Sets (1) and (2) (Table 8.2), with $v = 0.080$ ms^{-1} and $d = 0$.

Infiltration characteristic:	(1)	(2)	ΔR_{ac}
Accumulated runoff volume R_{ac} (m³):	19,411	20,356	0.945

Table 8.5 Comparison of annual runoff volumes, R_v (m³), from a runoff area of 20 m², predicted by Runoff Depth Model (D) ($\omega = 0.25$), with $\delta = 5.75$ mm (left side of table) and 6.00 mm (right side of table), and by Kinematic Wave Model (B) (Parameter Set (2) (Table 8.2), with $v = 0.080$ ms^{-1} and $d = 0$), for the years 1970-1983 at Niamey.

Year	P (mm)	$\delta = 5{,}75$ mm			$\delta = 6{,}00$ mm		
		R_v (D)	R_v (B)	ΔR_v	R_v (D)	R_v (B)	ΔR_v
70	482	1.711	1.872	-0.160	1.685	1.872	-0.187
71	455	1.455	1.085	0.370	1.428	1.085	0.343
72	236	0.589	0.484	0.105	0.569	0.484	0.085
73	382	1.261	1.539	-0.278	1.240	1.539	-0.299
74	466	1.708	1.185	0.523	1.685	1.185	0.500
75	668	2.311	1.796	0.516	2.273	1.796	0.477
76	563	2.034	0.771	1.263	2.008	0.771	1.234
77	577	2.103	1.723	0.380	2.075	1.723	0.352
78	532	1.863	2.175	-0.312	1.835	2.175	-0.340
80	392	1.133	1.237	-0.105	1.103	1.237	-0.134
81	464	1.738	2.935	-1.198	1.715	2.935	-1.220
82	319	0.941	1.220	-0.279	0.920	1.220	-0.300
83	430	1.548	2.334	-0.787	1.525	2.334	-0.809
Sum	5966	20.395	20.356	**0.039**	20.061	20.356	**-0.295**

Runoff predictions by the Runoff-Depth Model (D) and the Kinematic-Wave Model (B) were compared for different combinations of parameter values. For a small runoff area of 4 x 5 m², depression storage, d, was set at zero. The threshold value, δ, was varied until a value was found for which the difference in runoff predicted by the two models was minimal. Table 8.5 shows an example of such a comparison, where a *minimal difference* was found.

On the left-hand side of Table 8.5, δ is 5.75 mm, and the third column shows runoff volumes predicted by Model (D). The fourth column shows runoff volumes predicted by Model (B) for the given parameter values. The fifth column shows the difference between the two. The bottom line gives the total over 13 years, which is only 0.039 m³.

Since the parameter values are only estimates of the real values that occur in the field, it was decided to take *6 mm as the threshold value, δ,* for all the predictions made in this study by the Runoff-Depth Model (D), whereas for the *runoff coefficient, ω, 0.25* was used. The right side of Table 8.5 shows the predicted runoff for a 6 mm threshold. The difference in runoff predicted by both models over 13 years increased to 0.295 m³, which is very small (1.5%).

For the parameter values finally used in Table 8.5 (ω is 0.25 and δ is 6 mm), the runoff efficiency from 20 m^2 over the 13 years was calculated as the ratio of the total volume of runoff to the total volume of rainfall. A *runoff efficiency of 0.17* was found. This value was checked with runoff efficiencies reported in literature for sloping catchments of comparable dimensions.

Table 8.6 shows these values for various soil conditions and rainfall regimes. All these areas received minimal surface treatment. Average runoff efficiencies, e_{av}, *range from 0.09 to 0.26* and there seems to be a tendency towards higher values on steeper slopes. This is understandable since steeper slopes allow less time for infiltration and may have a lower depression storage.

There is no clear relationship between average runoff efficiency and rainfall regime. Many soils without a protective vegetative cover form a *surface crust* when they are exposed to rainfall. This crust then controls the infiltration rate and affects the runoff efficiency. The values of the infiltration parameters (Table 8.2) that were selected to predict runoff take this effect into account.

Table 8.6 Average runoff efficiencies, e_{av}, calculated as the ratio of runoff to rainfall volumes from catchments with area, A (m^2), and slope, s_0 (%), on soils that received minimal surface treatment in various rainfall regimes, P (mm). P_{ac} (mm) indicates the total rainfall accumulated during the observation period.

Location	Year	Soil	P	P_{ac}	Area	S_0	e_{av}
01. Sede Boqer	1982/1983	Silt Loam	90	140	116	1	0.19
02. Gran.Reef	1964-1976	Sandy Loam	210	2520	180		0.25
03. Kalgoorlie	1980/1981	Loam	255	255	40	1	0.18
04. Jodhpur	1975-1979	Loamy Sand	360	2793	72	.5	0.11
05. Jodhpur	1975-1979	Loamy Sand	360	2793	99	.5	0.20
06. Jodhpur	1975-1979	Loamy Sand	360	2793	144	.5	0.19
07. Mlingano	1979/1980	SaCla Loam	1100	793	20	10	0.12
08. Mlingano	1979/1980	SaCla Loam	1100	793	20	19	0.15
09. Mlingano	1979/1980	SaCla Loam	1100	793	20	22	0.13
10. Ibadan	1977+1978	Sandy Loam	1100	2008	20	1	0.14
11. Ibadan	1977+1978	Sandy Loam	1100	2008	40	1	0.18
12. Ibadan	1977+1978	Sandy Loam	1100	2008	60	1	0.21
13. Ibadan	1977+1978	Sandy Loam	1100	2008	80	1	0.08
14. Ibadan	1977+1978	Sandy loam	1100	2008	40	5	0.24
15. Ibadan	1977+1978	Sandy Loam	1100	2008	60	5	0.23
16. Ibadan	1977+1978	Sandy loam	1100	2008	80	5	0.16
17. Ibadan	1977+1978	Sandy Loam	1100	2008	40	10	0.24
18. Ibadan	1977+1978	Sandy loam	1100	2008	60	10	0.18
19. Ibadan	1977+1978	Sandy Loam	1100	2008	80	10	0.20
20. Ibadan	1977+1978	Sandy Loam	1100	2008	40	15	0.26
21. Ibadan	1977+1978	Sandy Loam	1100	2008	60	15	0.15
22. Ibadan	1977+1978	Sandy Loam	1100	2008	80	15	0.15
23. Nsukka	1979	Sand	1700	1946	60	5	0.09
24. Nsukka	1980	Sand	1700	1830	60	5	0.11
25. Owerri	1987	Sandy Loam	2250	2020	88	9	0.10
26. Owerri	1988	Sandy Loam	2250	2362	88	9	0.16

Overall average runoff efficiency: 0.17

1: Boers et al. (1986), 2: Fink et al. (1979), 3: Pepper & Morrissey (1985), 4-6: Sharma et al. (1982), 7-9: Ngatunga et al. (1984), 10-22: Lal (1983), 23 & 24: Obi (1982), 25 & 26: Boers et al. (1988).

The total accumulated rainfall during the observation period, P_{ac}, shows that most runoff efficiencies were measured over roughly 2 m of rainfall. The lower values for Sede Boqer, Kalgoorlie, and Mlingano are exceptions. The overall average of all these different e_{av}-values is 0.17. From this value, it was concluded that the parameter values selected for predictions by the Runoff Depth Model (ω 0.25 and δ 6.00 mm) in Table 8.5, which resulted in the same runoff efficiency of 0.17, are *realistic estimates*.

8.2   Micro-Catchment Design Predictions by SWATRE at Niamey

For the micro-catchment design predictions, one Neem tree in a windbreak identical to the experimental windbreak at Sadoré (Figure 7.1) was considered. For this windbreak design, the *basin area was fixed at 8 m²*. Little work has been done on the transpiration of windbreaks (Brenner et al. 1991). Neem can grow in hot and dry regions without irrigation and can be established in areas with annual rainfall, P, varying from 450 to 750 mm. Optimum growth is attained in areas with P of 1150 mm, whereas at least 130 mm a^{-1} is needed for survival. Neem requires 450 mm a^{-1} for good growth and tolerates a drought period of several months (Benge 1988; FAO 1974).

The micro-catchment design should aim at minimizing the losses in Equation 3, but, as was shown in Chapter 6, losses cannot be eliminated altogether. The best design approach is to aim at *sufficient water in an average year* and to allow deep percolation losses in wet years and some water shortages in dry years. Neem can overcome the dry years. In the absence of precise requirements of T_{act} for Neem, the above-mentioned data on rainfall requirements were used as the minimum requirements for design in terms of T_{act} needed for tree survival and growth.

Requirements for survival:

T_{act} (average year)	$\geq$ 130 mm	(86a)
T_{act} (dry year)	$\geq$ 130 mm	(86b)

Requirements for minimum growth:

T_{act} (average year)	$\geq$ 450 mm	(87a)
T_{act} (dry year)	$\geq$ 130 mm	(87b)

Requirements for good growth:

T_{act} (average year)	$\geq$ 450 mm	(88a)
T_{act} (dry year)	$\geq$ 450 mm	(88b)

With the basin area fixed at 8 m², T_{act} for the survival requirement in Equation 86 would be equivalent to about 1 m³ water, whereas for the minimum and good growth requirements in Equations 87a and 87b, T_{act} would have to be equivalent to about 3.6 m³. The assumption is that, under rainwater harvesting, *roots will develop vertically* rather than horizontally. To take up the soil water stored deep in the profile, roots will grow deep rather than wide and will remain in the wet soil volume under the basin.

For the present windbreak, only the size of the runoff area has to be found. The following design procedure was used. *For rainfall only,* the rooting depth of the tree was determined as described in Section 7.2. Then T_{act} was calculated for selected average, wet, and dry years and compared with the requirements in Equations 86, 87, and 88.

For rainfall and runoff, the rooting depth of the tree was found for an estimated size of runoff area. Then T_{act} was calculated for selected average and dry years and compared with Equations 86, 87, and 88. If T_{act} was below the target, the runoff area was increased and T_{act} was re-calculated. This procedure was repeated until the target in Equations 86, 87, and 88 was attained.

Water Balance Predictions by SWATRE and Runoff Models (B) and (D)
The annual rainfall data from Niamey were given in Table 8.1. The average over these thirteen years was 459 mm. Rainfall in 1974/75 was 466 mm, so this year was taken as an *average year* for the prediction of T_{act}. In 1972/73, rainfall was 236 mm, so that year was taken as a *dry year,* with a probability of exceedance of 98%. For a *wet year,* 1975/76 was taken, because, with its 668 mm of rainfall, it was the wettest year in the series, with an 8% probability of exceedance.

The daily evaporation data required for SWATRE were not available for Niamey, but were available from Class A pan readings done at Sadoré. As evaporation is less variable in space and time than rainfall, it was assumed that, in the absence of other data, the Class A pan readings from Sadoré could represent the evaporation at Niamey. For each day, the average open water evaporation was estimated by taking that day's average from the eight years of Sadoré records. In this way, an *average evaporation year* was constructed and was used for the three selected years at Niamey.

For Niamey, water-balance predictions of one Neem tree in a windbreak were made with runoff predicted by the Runoff Depth Model (D) and the Kinematic Wave Model (B). The difference between them and the prediction of T_{act} by SWATRE was studied. Parameter values used for the calibration at Sadoré (Table 7.1) were also applied to Niamey.

Table 8.7 shows the predicted R and T_{act} for the *average year* 1974/75. The first column shows rainfall only. Rooting depth was calculated at 3.0 m and T_{act} at 317 mm, which is about 25% of T_{pot}.

So in this average year at Niamey with rainfall only, T_{act} could not reach the minimum growth requirement of 450 mm a^{-1} in Equation 87a. Table 8.8 shows that in the dry year 1972/73 for rainfall only, T_{act} was 112 mm, which is below the survival requirement of 130 mm a^{-1} in Equation 86b. The second column in Table 8.7 shows runoff R from a runoff area of 20 m², as predicted by the Runoff Depth Model (D).

Table 8.7 Rainfall, P, predicted R, and T_{act} (mm) for one Neem tree in a windbreak at Niamey during the *average year* 1974/75, for rainfall only and for rainfall and runoff from runoff areas of 20 m² and 40 m², predicted by Runoff Depth Model (D) and Kinematic Wave Model (B).

	Rain only	Rainfall and runoff			
		(D) 20 m²	(B) 20 m²	(D) 40 m²	(B) 40 m²
P	466	466	466	466	466
R	0	211	144	421	291
T_{act}	317	530	469	706	610

84

Table 8.8 Rainfall, **P**, predicted **R**, and T_{act} (mm) for one Neem tree in a windbreak at Niamey during the *dry year* 1972/73, for rainfall only and for rainfall and runoff from runoff areas of 20 m² and 40 m², predicted by Runoff Depth Model (D) and Kinematic Wave Model (B).

	Rain only	Rainfall and runoff			
		(D) 20 m²	(B) 20 m²	(D) 40 m²	(B) 40 m²
P	230	230	230	230	230
R	0	**71**	**59**	**142**	118
T_{act}	112	**185**	**176**	**247**	217

Rooting depth was calculated at 4.0 m. Runoff was 211 mm, which was used to increase T_{act} from 317 mm to 530 mm. With this runoff, the minimum growth requirement in Equation 87a was reached. *Runoff was used very efficiently,* increasing T_{act} without loss.

Figure 8.2 shows the predicted T_{act}, for the average year 1974/75 for rainfall only, and for rainfall supplemented by runoff from 20 m², as predicted by Runoff Depth

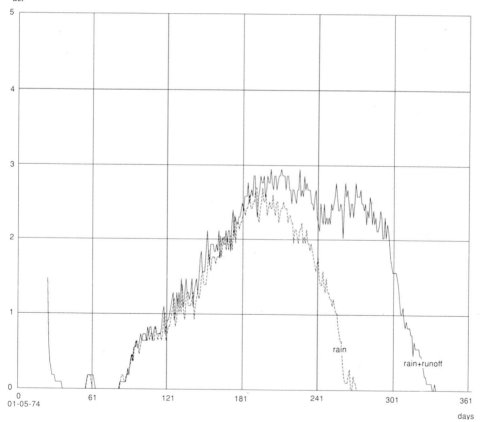

Figure 8.2 SWATRE predicted actual transpiration T_{act} at Niamey, Niger, during the average year 1974/75 for rainfall only and for rainfall supplemented by runoff from 20 m².

Model (D). Runoff water supplied during the rainy season is stored in the rootzone, and the *period of active soil water uptake in the dry season is extended by about 80 days.*

The third column of Table 8.7 gives a runoff prediction, R, of 144 mm by the Kinematic Wave Model (B), which is more conservative than the Runoff Depth Model (D). This is due to the effect of *low-intensity storms,* which do not generate runoff, but for which the Runoff Depth Model (D) predicts runoff. Calculated rooting depth is 3.6 m. Predicted T_{act} is 469 mm, which is lower than in Column 2, but still enough to reach the minimum development requirement in Equation 87a.

Table 8.8 shows that, for the *dry year 1972/73,* the Runoff Depth Model (D) predicted 71 mm of runoff, which increased T_{act} to 185 mm and exceeded the minimum development requirement in Equation 87b. The value of R predicted by the Kinematic Wave Model (B) was 59 mm. This resulted in $T_{act} = 176$ mm, which also reached the minimum development requirement in Equation 87b. So with a runoff area of 20 m², *minimum development can be realized.*

For the dry year 1972/73, Figure 8.3 shows the predicted T_{act} for rainfall only, and

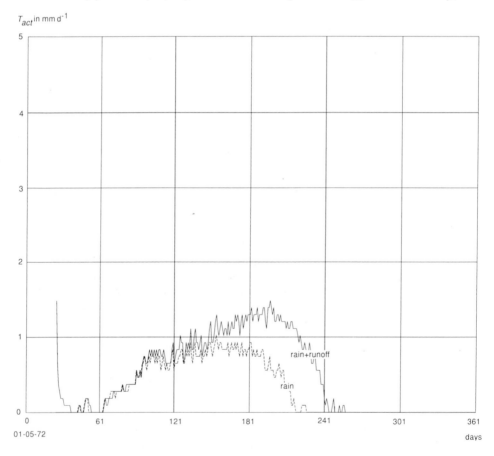

Figure 8.3 SWATRE predicted actual transpiration T_{act} at Niamey, Niger, during the dry year 1972/73 for rainfall only and for rainfall supplemented by runoff from 20 m².

86

Table 8.9 Rainfall, P, predicted R, T_{act}, and D (mm) for one Neem tree in a windbreak at Niamey during the *wet year* 1975/76, for rainfall only and for rainfall and runoff from runoff areas of 20 m² and 40 m², predicted by Runoff Depth Model (D) and Kinematic Wave Model (B).

	Rain only	Rainfall and runoff			
		(D) 20 m²	(B) 20 m²	(D) 40 m²	(B) 40 m²
P	668	668	668	668	668
R	0	284	220	**568**	442
T_{act}	**449**	**623**	**605**	796	733
D	34	**161**	**121**	**262**	199

for rainfall supplemented by runoff from 20 m² as predicted by Runoff Depth Model (D). The extension by 20 days of the period of active soil-water uptake is less spectacular than in the average year (Figure 8.2), but, *in a dry year, the extra 73 mm of actual transpiration is very important* for tree development. The rainy season often starts with high-intensity bursts of convective storms, which effectively generate runoff. This is shown on Day 1, when T_{act} immediately jumped to 1.5 mm d⁻¹.

Table 8.9 shows predicted R, T_{act}, and D for the *wet year 1975/76*. With rainfall only, T_{act} was 449 mm, which satisfies the growth requirement of 450 mm a⁻¹. So in this wet year, runoff was not needed, and a deep-percolation loss, D, of 34 mm even occurred. With a runoff area of 20 m², T_{act} will increase to 623 mm (Runoff Depth Model) or 605 mm (Kinematic Wave Model), but D will increase to 161 mm and 121 mm, respectively. So in the wet year, almost *half the generated runoff, R, is lost to percolation, D*.

Good growth could only be realized by enlarging the runoff area and thereby attaining the requirement of 450 mm a⁻¹ in Equation 88b. A runoff area of 40 m² was tried, which, in the dry year 1972/73 (Table 8.8), generated 142 mm of runoff (Runoff Depth Model) and brought T_{act} to 247 mm, *about 50% of the target* in Equation 88b. Runoff generated during the wet year 1975/76 (Table 8.9) was 568 mm (Runoff Depth Model), but 262 mm was lost to deep percolation, D.

Any further enlargement of the runoff area to attain the good growth target in Equation 88b would cause excessive deep percolation losses, D, in a wet year such as 1975/76. Also, it would be *difficult to store larger quantities of runoff water* during infiltration in the basin area. A runoff area of about 40 m² seems the best option for Niamey. This will guarantee minimum tree development (Equation 87), will provide 50% of the requirement for good growth (Equation 88), and will limit deep percolation.

8.3   Conclusion on Runoff Prediction and Micro-Catchment Design

The conclusion from the predictions at Niamey are that, with a runoff area of 20 m², the minimum development requirement in Equation 87 can be satisfied. With a runoff area of 40 m², 50% of the requirement for good growth in Equation 88 can be satisfied. To realize good growth completely, which is a severe condition, the runoff area should be larger than 40 m². Theoretically, it would be possible to satisfy the requirements of Equation 88, but this would cause excessive deep percolation and problems of basin storage in wet years. *A runoff area of ± 40 m² seems the best option.*

A comparison of the runoff predicted by the Runoff Depth Model (D) and the Kinematic Wave Model (B) shows that, with the selected parameter values, the Runoff Depth Model gives a more optimistic runoff estimate. Nevertheless, the predictions do not differ dramatically and would seem to be realistic. When the predicted runoff is routed through SWATRE, the differences in R are translated into differences in T_{act}, but again the result seems realistic. From this comparison, it could be concluded that, in regions where storm-intensity data are not available, *the Runoff Depth Model (D) is a good alternative to the Kinematic Wave Model (B).*

9   Prediction of Micro-Catchment Design in Semi-Arid Zones of Niger and Nigeria

9.1   The Physical Environment

The West African Republic of *Niger* lies within the northern tropics, between 11°33′N and 23°33′N. It is bordered on the north by Algeria and Libya, on the west by Mali and Burkina Faso, on the south by Benin and Nigeria, and on the east by Chad (Figure 9.1). In northern *Nigeria*, the border with Niger is formed by the states of Sokoto (northwest), Katsina (north central), and Borno (northeast).

South of parallel 16°N stretches a region of about 400,000 km² – an area of plains of low relief, dissected by fossil or seasonal valleys, and with rocky outliers here and there. Living in this region is almost the entire population of Niger, totalling several million people. In the west, the River Niger cuts through a very level plain that lies at about 200 m above mean sea level. This plain has widespread surfaces of laterite. Most of its soils are of sandy or clayey-sand composition. The desert soils produced by wind erosion are poor in chemical constituents.

Niger has rainfall in summer and a dry season in winter. Between the 8th and the 14th parallels, a typical tropical or savannah climate prevails. Farther away from the equator, the rainy season becomes shorter and the dry season longer. The dry season

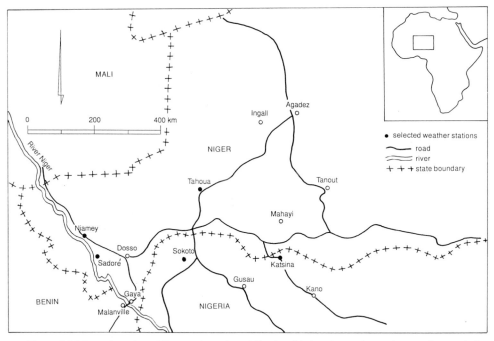

Figure 9.1 Map of southern Niger and northern Nigeria with locations where micro-catchment design predictions were made indicated by black dots.

starts with a hot and dry continental wind, known as the *harmattan*. Characteristic of this region is the savannah – a prairie of hardy grasses that stand 1 to 3 m tall. After the rainy season, in the northern savannah, the grass dries out and yields to bare soil (Sivakumar et al.1979).

In Arabic, *Sahel* means 'shore', which refers to the area facing the Sahara Desert. The Sahelian *sub-desert* climate marks the transition from a tropical to a desert climate. Near the tropics, between 14 °N and 18 °N, rain falls for a short period of three months, and sometimes for only a few weeks. Rainfall varies from year to year. Near the 20th northern parallel, the intertropical convergence zone (i.e. the moving area of contact between dry tropical air and humid equatorial air) disappears and the desert begins. The desert vegetation is adapted to long dry periods: roots are large and deep, organs of evaporation are small, and grasses are hard and short.

Figure 9.2 shows the mean annual rainfall in Niger. Isohyets run more or less parallel. North of the 16th parallel, the region is completely dry, whereas to the south the distance between isohyets decreases and the rainfall gradient steepens. The mean annual rainfall at 77% of 75 stations varies from 300 to 600 mm. The general pattern of rainfall during the rainy season is similar to the annual pattern shown in Figure 9.2, which indicates that distribution tends to be *monomodal*. Most of the rain (90 to 95%) falls in a single season that extends from June to September. The length of this season in a particular location depends to a large extent on the latitude of that location.

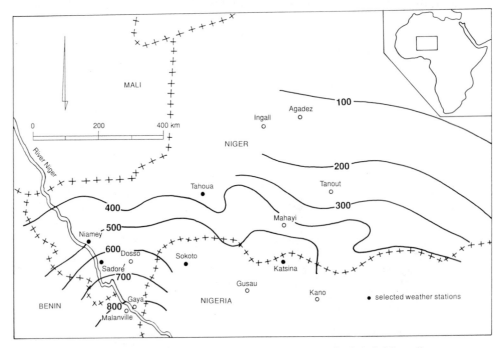

Figure 9.2 Mean annual rainfall in southern Niger. From north to south, the rainfall gradient steepens from approximately 50 mm per 100 km in the north to approximately 200 mm per 100 km in the south, as shown by decreasing isohyet spacing (see also Figure 1.5).

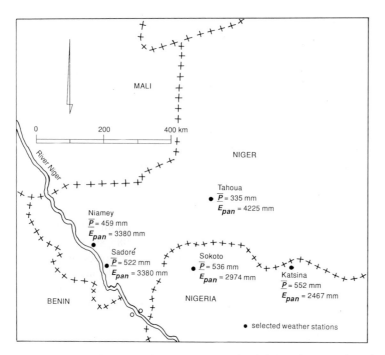

Figure 9.3 Approximate location, average annual rainfall, and evaporation of places used for micro-catchment design predictions.

Objectives of Micro-Catchment Design Predictions

The *objectives* of the micro-catchment design predictions are:
- To investigate whether rainwater harvesting from micro-catchments can *increase T_{act} for favourable tree growth*, by inducing and collecting runoff water, and storing and conserving it as soil water to bridge dry periods;
- To *determine the best size of a runoff area* to satisfy the first objective.

All design predictions were made for a windbreak similar to the experimental windbreak at Sadoré, which was used to calibrate the model in Chapter 7. SWATRE was used to predict the actual transpiration and other components of the *water balance for one Neem tree in a basin area of 8 m² in such a windbreak*. Runoff was predicted with Runoff Depth Model (D). Figure 9.3 shows the approximate locations of places where data were available. The data from Sadoré were used in Chapter 7; those from Niamey were used in Chapter 8. The present chapter will present micro-catchment design predictions for *Sadoré and Tahoua in Niger and for Sokoto and Katsina in Nigeria*.

The results of the water balance and micro-catchment design predictions for Sadoré will be discussed in some detail. For the other locations, the discussion will be restricted to the final results.

9.2 Prediction of Micro-Catchment Design at Sadoré, Niger

Rainfall and Evaporation

Table 9.1 shows the annual rainfall for the eight hydrological years for which daily rainfall data were available from the ICRISAT Sahelian Centre at Sadoré. The average over these eight years was 522 mm. Used as examples in the prediction of micro-catchment design were the following: the average year 1985/86, with P is 545 mm; the *dry year* 1984/85, with P is 258 mm (95% probability of exceedance); and the *wet year* 1986/87, with P is 673 mm (18% probability of exceedance).

Table 9.1 also shows E_{pan} at Sadoré with an *average of 3380 mm*. The highest values occurred during the dry year 1984/85 (3861 mm) and the average year 1985/86 (3740 mm). The lowest values occurred in the wet years 1988/89 (2750 mm) and 1989/90 (2756 mm).

The wet year 1986/87 showed E_{pan} equal to 3462, which is about 80 mm higher than the average of these eight years. In the average rainfall year 1985/86, E_{pan} equalled 3740 mm, which is about 260 mm above the average. For rainwater harvesting, rainfall is considered more important than evaporation, so it was accepted that E_{pan} values were higher than average. In the three selected years, the *data were consistent* in the sense that the trend in rainfall was opposite to that in Class A pan evaporation.

Application of SWATRE

SWATRE was used as in Chapter 7 with the *same procedures and parameter values* (Table 7.1) that were calculated for soil water withdrawal, S_{max}, in Equation 71; for T_{pot}, ET_{pot}, E_{pot}, and ET_0 in Equations 72 to 75; for the initial condition of θ_0 in Equation 76; for the lower boundary condition in Equation 67; for the upper boundary condition in Equation 77; for the interception loss, E_i, from Equations 78 to 82; for the water evaporation, E_w, and for the rooting depth, $|z_r|$. Soil conditions, including $K(\theta)$ and $h(\theta)$, were as in Chapter 7.

Water Balance Prediction: Rainfall Only

Table 9.2 shows the water balance, for rainfall only, for one Neem tree in a windbreak at Sadoré during *the average year 1985/86, the dry year 1984/85, and the wet year 1986/87*. Annual rainfall, P, in 1985/86 was 545 mm, of which 22 mm was intercepted as E_i, leaving net rainfall, P_n, equal to 523 mm. Since runoff, R, is zero, P_n is equal to infiltration, I. Actual transpiration, T_{act}, was 409 mm, E_{act}, was 133 mm, and D was zero. In the dry year 1984/85, P was 258 mm, which results in a T_{act} of 138 mm, whereas E_{act} and D remained the same as in 1985/86.

In the wet year 1986/87, P was 673 mm, which gives a T_{act} of 481 mm. This value exceeds the *survival requirement* of T_{act} in Equation 86 ($\geq$ 130 mm for *average and dry years*), but is less than the *minimum growth requirement of* T_{act} in Equation 87a

Table 9.1 Annual rainfall, P, and E_{pan} (mm) at *Sadoré, Niger*, for eight hydrological years (1 May-30 April) from 1982/83 to 1989/90.

Year	82/83	83/84	84/85	85/86	86/87	87/88	88/89	89/90	Average
P	377	598	258	545	673	438	662	623	522
E_{pan}	3786	3380	3861	3740	3462	3305	2750	2756	3380

Table 9.2 Predicted annual water balance (rainfall only) for one Neem tree in a windbreak at *Sadoré, Niger* in different year types.

	P (mm)	E_i (mm)	P_n (mm)	R (mm)	I (mm)	T_{act} (mm)	E_{act} (mm)	D (mm)
Average year 1985/1986	545	22	523	0	523	**409**	133	0
Dry year 1984/1985	258	14	244	0	244	**138**	133	0
Wet year 1986/1987	673	29	644	0	644	**481**	180	0

(≥ 450 mm for an *average year*). This was caused by an unfavourable distribution of rainfall in that year. In all three years, E_i was small. In the dry year, T_{act} and E_{act} were of the same order. In the other years, E_{act} was 33 to 37% of T_{act}.

Micro-Catchment Design Prediction: Rainfall and Runoff

Table 9.3 shows P, R, T_{act}, and D, in the same three years as above, for rainfall only (first column, data taken from Table 9.2), for rainfall and runoff from 20 m² (second column), and for rainfall and runoff from 40 m² (third column). In 1985/86, a runoff area of 20 m² supplied 232 mm of runoff water to the basin area, which increased T_{act} to 633 mm. In the dry year 1984/85, R was 78 mm and T_{act} was 205 mm. *The minimum growth requirement was now easily reached.* For good growth, the requirement in Equation 88b is a T_{act} (dry year) of ≥ 450 mm. A runoff area of 40

Table 9.3 Annual rainfall, P, and predicted R, T_{act}, and D (mm) for one Neem tree in a windbreak at *Sadoré, Niger*, for rainfall only and for rainfall and runoff from 20 m² and 40 m² in different year types.

	Rainfall only	Rainfall and runoff	
Average year		Runoff area 20 m²	Runoff area 40 m²
P (85/86)	545	545	545
R	0	232	465
T_{act}	**409**	633	755
D	0	5	113
Dry year		Runoff area 20 m²	Runoff area 40 m²
P (84/85)	258	258	258
R	0	78	155
T_{act}	**138**	205	277
D	0	0	0
Wet year		Runoff area 20 m²	Runoff area 40 m²
P (86/87)	673	673	673
R	0	**285**	**571**
T_{act}	481	720	849
D	0	**38**	**185**

93

m² would supply 155 mm of runoff water, which would bring T_{act} to 277 mm, still not enough for good growth.

Figure 9.4 shows predicted T_{act} during the average year 1985/86 for rainfall only, and for rainfall supplemented by runoff from 20 m² as predicted by the Runoff Depth Model (D). Stored runoff water enables tree water uptake for an extra 30 days in the dry season. During the dry year 1984/85, runoff water from an area of 20 m² extended the period of root water uptake by 40 days (Figure 9.5). In addition, T_{act} increased. Figures 9.4 and 9.5 clearly show the *importance of runoff water, especially during dry years*.

Although it is possible to increase the runoff area until the good growth target is reached, a larger area will create problems during the wet year 1986/87, as the bottom of Table 9.3 shows. A runoff area of 20 m² supplies 285 mm of runoff water, which increases T_{act} by almost the same quantity, but now deep percolation, *D*, starts at 38 mm. A runoff area of 40 m² generates twice as much runoff water (571 mm), but now *D* is 185 mm. The increase in T_{act} is only 129 mm, *so runoff water is not being used efficiently*.

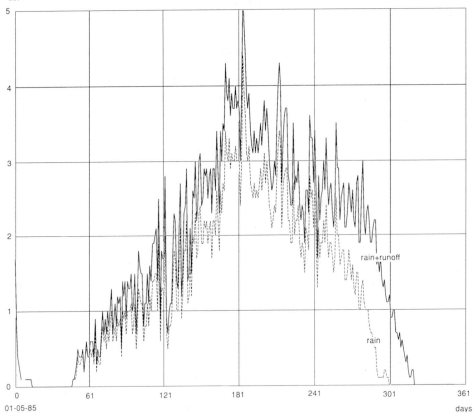

Figure 9.4 SWATRE predicted actual transpiration T_{act} at Sadoré, Niger, during the average year 1985/86 for rainfall only and for rainfall supplemented by runoff from 20 m².

94

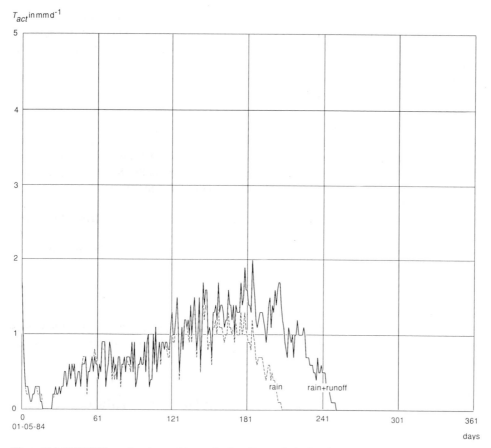

T_{act} in mm d^{-1}

Figure 9.5 SWATRE predicted actual transpiration T_{act} at Sadoré, Niger, during the dry year 1984/85 for rainfall only and for rainfall supplemented by runoff from 20 m^2.

The water-holding capacity of the soil, θ_{FC}-θ_{WP}, is very limited: 0.11 for the top layer and 0.07 for the bottom layer. The rooting depth, $|z_r|$, in an average year with runoff from 20 m^2 would be 5 m, and W_{max}, according to Equation 7, would then only be 470 mm. Besides a low water-holding capacity, this soil has a high hydraulic conductivity, which enhances deep percolation in wet years. And there is yet another problem: if the runoff area were to be enlarged, storage of runoff water would become difficult and the basin might overflow. For these reasons, the *runoff area should not be increased beyond 20 m^2*.

Conclusion on Micro-Catchment Design at Sadoré
The conclusion from the predictions at Sadoré is that the *minimum growth requirement* in Equation 87 can easily be satisfied with a runoff area of 20 m^2. Achieving *good growth* as in Equation 88 is theoretically possible, but it will create problems of basin storage and deep percolation losses in wet years. Therefore, to achieve 100% of good growth is too severe a condition, and it should be accepted that there will be reduced

95

tree growth in dry years and some deep percolation in wet years. For each tree in the windbreak *at Sadoré, the best runoff area is about 20 m²*. Since the tree spacing is 4 m, this means a 5-m-wide runoff strip for one row of trees along the length of the windbreak.

Since the realization of good growth is less than 100%, the achievement may be quantified by defining:

$$\Gamma = T_{act}/T_{target} \tag{89}$$

where Γ is the achievement ratio (–), restricted to $0 \le \Gamma \le 1$, and T_{target} (L) is the target set for T_{act}, with the restriction that, when Equation 89 is being applied to each of the limits defining a growth condition (as in Equations 86, 87, and 88), Γ *takes the lowest value*. Applying Equation 89 to the values of T_{act} in Table 9.3, we have:

– For survival, Γ is 1.0;
– For minimum growth, Γ is 0.9 (rainfall only) and Γ is 1.0 (runoff from 20 m² and 40 m²);
– For good growth, Γ is 0.3 (rainfall only), Γ is 0.5 (runoff from 20 m²), and Γ is 0.6 (runoff from 40 m²).

These values are summarized in Table 9.12.

Achievement Ratio for Niamey
Applying Equation 89 to the values of T_{act} in Tables 8.7, 8.8, and 8.9 gives the values of Γ for Niamey. These values are similar to those for Sadoré and are summarized in Table 9.12

9.3   Prediction of Micro-Catchment Design at Tahoua, Niger

Rainfall and Evaporation
Table 9.4 shows the annual rainfall of thirteen hydrological years (1972 to 1984) at Tahoua, Niger, for which daily rainfall data were available. The average of this series was 335 mm, about 200 mm less than the average at Sadoré. Three years were selected for the design predictions: *the average year 1981/82* (P is 344 mm), *the dry year 1982/83* (more than 100 mm below average and 90% probability of exceedance), and *the wet year 1978/79* (almost 200 mm above average and 6% probability of exceedance).

Daily evaporation data were not available for Tahoua, so the average of the eight-year Sadoré E_{pan} records, which was used for Niamey (Chapter 8), was used to engineer the evaporation data required for SWATRE. Monthly potential evapotranspiration data from Tahoua were used to estimate the ratio of potential evapotranspiration at Tahoua over Sadoré. *This ratio was applied to calculate E_{pan} at Tahoua*. The ratio varied from 1.37 (June) to 1.13 (February), with an annual average of 1.25.

Table 9.4 Annual rainfall, P, (mm) at *Tahoua, Niger,* for thirteen hydrological years (1 May-30 April) from 1972/73 to 1984/85.

Year	72/	73/	74/	75/	76/	77/	78/	79/	80/	81/	82/	83/	84/
P	265	244	421	421	392	403	**523**	295	319	**344**	**219**	254	257

Table 9.5 Textural characteristics of a *loamy fine sand* from Mali, common in the Sahel (Hoogmoed 1985).

Clay $< 2\,\mu$	Silt $2\text{-}50\,\mu$	Very fine sand $50\text{-}105\,\mu$	Fine sand $105\text{-}210\,\mu$	Coarse sand $210\text{-}2000\,\mu$
5	15	35	25	20

Application of SWATRE

SWATRE was used with the Tahoua data as it was with the Sadoré data, with the same procedures and parameter values (Table 7.1), except for the soil hydraulic parameters $K(\theta)$ and $h(\theta)$. A type of soil that is widespread in the Sahel Zone (Hoogmoed 1991) – a loamy fine sand – was used to specify the soil hydraulic parameters. Table 9.5 summarizes the textural characteristics of this soil. The retention curve of this soil was compared with that of standard soils of the Staring Series (Wösten et al. 1987), and was found to correspond to Subsoil O2 (see Figure 9.6). The water-holding capacity, $\theta_{FC}\text{-}\theta_{WP}$, is 0.14 for the Sahel soil and 0.17 for the Staring soil. The $K(\theta)$ and $h(\theta)$ relationships of the Staring Subsoil O2 were used for the design prediction.

Micro-Catchment Design Prediction

Table 9.6 shows P, R, T_{act}, and D in the three selected years in Tahoua, for rainfall only (first column), for rainfall and runoff from 40 m² (second column), and for rainfall and runoff from 120 m² (third column). In 1981/82, P was 344 mm, which resulted in a T_{act} of 257 mm. In 1982/83, P was 219 mm, and T_{act} was 155 mm, so *the survival requirement was satisfied* with rainfall only. In the wet year 1978/79, the deep percolation from rainfall only was 129 mm.

To satisfy the minimum growth requirement, T_{act} should increase in 1981/82. The

Table 9.6 Annual rainfall, P, and predicted R, T_{act}, and D (mm) for one Neem tree in a windbreak at Tahoua, Niger, for rainfall only and for rainfall and runoff from 40 m² and 120 m² in different year types.

	Rainfall only	Rainfall and runoff	
Average year		Runoff area 40 m²	Runoff area 120 m²
P (81/82)	344	344	344
R	0	244	670
T_{act}	257	471	853
D	1	1	13
Dry year		Runoff area 40 m²	Runoff area 120 m²
P (82/83)	219	219	219
R	0	127	347
T_{act}	155	259	453
D	0	0	0
Wet year		Runoff area 40 m²	Runoff area 120 m²
P (78/79)	523	523	523
R	0	434	1189
T_{act}	290	503	875
D	129	325	681

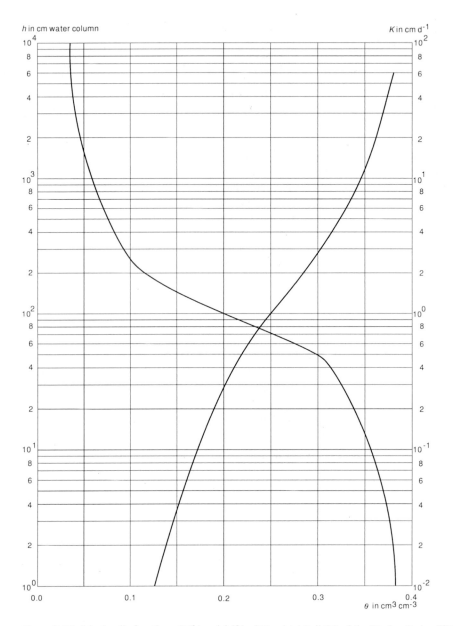

h in cm water column

K in cm d^{-1}

θ in cm3 cm-3

Figure 9.6 Soil hydraulic functions $K(\theta)$ and $h(\theta)$ of Standard Soil O2 of the Staring Series (Wösten et al.1987), assumed to represent a loamy fine sand at Tahoua. This type of soil is widespread in the Sahel zone.

second column shows that, with runoff from 40 m², T_{act} increased to 471 mm in 1981/82 and to 259 mm in 1982/83. This means that *minimum growth can be realized with a runoff area of 40 m².* But in the wet year 1978/79, D was 325 mm, which is 75% of the generated runoff. So runoff water is wasted. The water-holding capacity of the soil, θ_{FC}-θ_{WP}, is 0.17. Rooting depth in an average year, with runoff from 40 m², is 1.50 m, which means W_{max} is 255 mm. So in wet years, deep percolation below 1.50 m occurs. This is enhanced by the relatively high hydraulic conductivity of this soil.

Figure 9.7 shows predicted T_{act} in the average year 1981/82 for rainfall only, and for rainfall supplemented by runoff from an area of 40 m². The fluctuation of T_{act} under rainfall only indicates the dry conditions and the lack of soil-water storage. More available soil water supplied by runoff produces a more continuous pattern of T_{act} and an extension of the period of root water uptake, which results in *an increase in T_{act} of more than 80%*. During the dry year 1982/83 (not shown here), the runoff water produced a similar improvement in the transpiration pattern.

The last column in Table 9.6 shows what happens when the runoff area is 120 m² and *the good growth requirement is satisfied: T_{act}* surpasses the limit of 450 mm a⁻¹. The bottom of the table shows that R is 1189 mm and D is 681 mm. Compared with the 40 m² runoff area, R increased by 755 mm, but T_{act} increased only by 372 mm, and D more than doubled. So satisfying the water requirements for good growth *wastes runoff water and creates basin storage problems*, as was discussed for Sadoré.

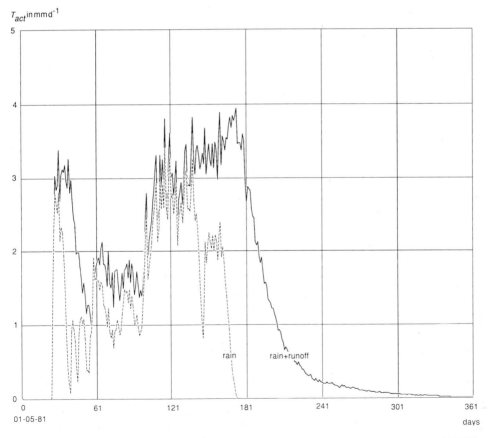

Figure 9.7 SWATRE predicted actual transpiration T_{act} at Tahoua, Niger, during the average year 1981/82 for rainfall only and for rainfall supplemented by runoff from 40 m².

99

It seems better to have a runoff area of about 40 m² at Tahoua and to accept a T_{act} below the good growth requirement in dry years like 1982/83.

Conclusion on Micro-Catchment Design at Tahoua
From the predictions at Tahoua, it appears that rainfall alone is enough for the survival of the Neem trees and that 20 m² can supply enough runoff water to satisfy their minimum growth requirements. Increasing the runoff area can improve growth conditions further, but achieving good growth conditions completely is not advisable, because runoff water will not be used efficiently, deep percolation will become excessive, and basin storage problems will arise. *The best runoff area for Tahoua is about 40 m².* The values of the achievement ratio, Γ, for Tahoua are summarized in Table 9.12.

9.4   Prediction of Micro-Catchment Design at Sokoto, Nigeria

Rainfall and Evaporation
For Sokoto, Nigeria, daily rainfall data were available for 14 hydrological years (1950-1963) (Haskoning 1991). Table 9.7 shows the annual totals. The average of this series was 536 mm, which is comparable to the annual rainfall at Sadoré and Niamey. For design predictions, the following three years were selected: *the average year* 1954/55 with P is 537 mm, *the dry year* 1950/51 with P is 315 mm (92% probability of exceedance), and *the wet year* 1952/54 with P is 830 mm – almost 300 mm above average (8% probability of exceedance).

Daily evaporation data were not available for the period of the rainfall records, so the average evaporation year, calculated from the eight years of Sadoré Class A Pan records, was used, as was done for Tahoua. Monthly potential evapotranspiration data from Sokoto were used to correct the Sadoré data, with the application of the ratio of potential evapotranspiration at Sokoto to that at Sadoré. This ratio was applied to calculate E_{pan} at Sokoto. The ratio varied from 0.93 (June) to 0.84 (February), with an annual average of 0.88.

Application of SWATRE
SWATRE was used for the Sokoto data as it was for the Sadoré data, with the same procedures and parameter values (Table 7.1) except for the soil hydraulic parameters $K(\theta)$ and $h(\theta)$. The hydraulic parameters $K(\theta)$ and $h(\theta)$ of the top soil in the area were available from MacDonald Agricultural Services (1991), and these data (Table 9.8 and Figure 9.8) were used for the predictions. The water-holding capacity, $\theta_{FC}-\theta_{WP}$, of the top soil is 0.14. For the sandy subsoil, hydraulic functions from Subsoil O5 of the Staring Series (Wösten et al. 1987) were applied (see Figure 7.2b), with a $\theta_{FC}-\theta_{WP}$ of 0.07. The thickness of the topsoil and subsoil were set at 3 m each.

Table 9.7 Annual rainfall, P, (mm) at *Sokoto, Nigeria*, for fourteen hydrological years (1 May-30 April) from 1950/51 to 1963/64.

Year	50/	51/	52/	53/	54/	55/	56/	57/	58/	59/	60/	61/	62/	63/	**Average**
P	315	437	**830**	820	**537**	418	461	551	582	339	364	628	720	496	**536**

100

Table 9.8 Textural characteristics of a *coarse sand* from north Sokoto (MacDonald Agricultural Services 1991).

Clay < 2 μ	Silt 2-50 μ	Fine sand 50-210 μ	Coarse sand 210-2000 μ
4	5	38	53

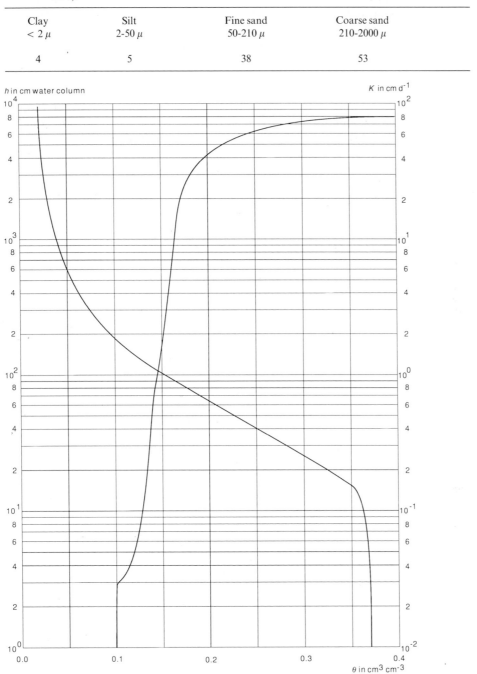

Figure 9.8 Soil hydraulic functions $K(\theta)$ and $h(\theta)$ of a sandy topsoil from Sokoto. The sandy subsoil was assumed similar to coarse sand, Standard Soil O5 of the Staring Series, see Fig. 7.2b (Wösten et al. 1987).

Micro-Catchment Design Prediction

Table 9.9 shows P, R, T_{act}, and D in the three selected Sokoto years, for rainfall only (first column) and for rainfall and runoff from 20 m^2 (second column). In 1954/55, P was 537 mm, which resulted in a T_{act} of 354 mm. In 1950/51, P was 315 mm and T_{act} was 207 mm, so *the survival requirements were satisfied* with rainfall only. In the wet year 1952/53, deep percolation of 271 mm occurred from rainfall only.

In 1954/55, T_{act} must increase to satisfy the minimum growth requirement. The second column shows that, with runoff from 20 m^2, T_{act} increased to 577 mm in 1954/55 and to 343 mm in 1950/51. This means that *minimum growth can be realized with a runoff area of 20 m^2*. But in the wet year 1952/53, D was 462 mm. Runoff from 20 m^2 is 391 mm, but this increases T_{act} by only 200 mm, and the remaining runoff water is lost to deep percolation. So runoff water is not being used efficiently, and increasing the runoff area to achieve complete good growth, as in Equation 88b, *increases deep percolation and creates basin storage problems*. This is not advisable.

The water-holding capacity of the soil is low. In an average year, with runoff from 20 m^2, the rooting depth is 5 m, which means W_{max} is 470 mm. The hydraulic conductivity is high, which enhances percolation through the profile. Figure 9.9 illustrates the effect of runoff water from 20 m^2 on T_{act} in the dry year 1950/51. Soil-water withdrawal is extended by 100 days, up to Day 330, at the end of March, and *roots take up water for almost the entire dry season*.

Conclusion on Micro-Catchment Design at Sokoto

The predictions at Sokoto indicate that Neem trees can survive on rainfall only. Runoff from 20 m^2 is enough to satisfy the minimum growth requirement. Increasing the runoff area can improve growth conditions further, but complete achievement of good growth is not advisable because of excessive deep percolation and basin storage

Table 9.9 Annual rainfall, P, and predicted R, T_{act}, and D (mm) of one Neem tree in a windbreak at Sokoto, Nigeria, for rainfall only and for rainfall and runoff from 20 m^2 in different year types.

	Rainfall only	Rainfall and runoff
Average year		Runoff area 20 m^2
P (54/55)	537	537
R	0	229
T_{act}	354	577
D	16	29
Dry year		Runoff area 20 m^2
P (50/51)	315	315
R	0	137
T_{act}	207	343
D	0	0
Wet year		Runoff area 20 m^2
P (52/53)	830	830
R	0	391
T_{act}	391	591
D	271	462

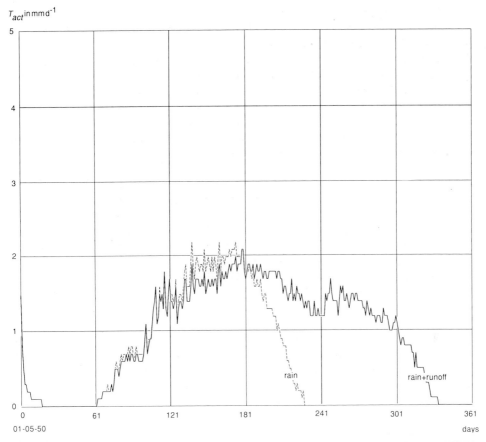

T_{act} in mm d^{-1}

01-05-50

days

Figure 9.9 SWATRE predicted actual transpiration T_{act} at Sokoto, Nigeria, during the dry year 1950/51 for rainfall only and for rainfall supplemented by runoff from 20 m^2.

problems. *The best runoff area for Sokoto is about 20 m^2*. Values of the achievement ratio, Γ, for Sokoto are summarized in Table 9.12.

9.5   Prediction of Micro-Catchment Design at Katsina, Nigeria

Daily rainfall data from 1970 to 1976 were available for Katsina, Nigeria (Haskoning 1991). Table 9.10 shows the annual rainfall totals for the seven hydrological years. The average was 552 mm. Three years were selected for design predictions: the *average*

Table 9.10 *Annual rainfall, **P**,* (mm) at *Katsina, Nigeria,* for seven hydrological years (1 May-30 April) from 1970/71 to 1976/77.

Year	70/71	71/72	72/73	73/74	74/75	75/76	76/77	Average
P	**706**	501	64	**430**	634	**560**	568	552

103

year 1975/76, with **P** is 560 mm, the *dry year* 1973/74, with **P** is 430 mm, more than 100 mm below the average (90% probability of exceedance), and the *wet year* 1970/71, with **P** is 706 mm, more than 150 mm above the average (9% probability of exceedance).

No daily evaporation data were available for the seven-year period of the rainfall record, so the average evaporation year of Sadoré was used, just as it was for Sokoto and Tahoua. Monthly potential evapotranspiration data from Katsina were applied to correct the Sadoré data, with the application of the ratio of potential evapotranspiration at Katsina to that at Sadoré. With this ratio, E_{pan} at Katsina was calculated. The ratio varied from 0.88 (June) to 0.56 (December), with an annual average of 0.73.

Application of SWATRE

SWATRE was used for the Katsina data as it was for the Sadoré data, with the same procedures and parameter values (Table 7.1), except for the soil hydraulic parameters $K(\theta)$ and $h(\theta)$. The soil-water retention characteristic $h(\theta)$ in the area was compared with standard soils of the Staring Series (Wösten et al. 1987; see Figure 7.2a). Subsoil O1 agreed well with these data and was used to define the hydraulic parameters, $K(\theta)$ and $h(\theta)$, for the topsoil and the subsoil. The water-holding capacity, $\theta_{FC}-\theta_{WP}$, is 0.09 for the Katsina soil and 0.11 for the Staring soil.

Micro-Catchment Design Prediction

Table 9.11 shows **P**, **R**, T_{act}, and **D** in the three selected Katsina years for rainfall only (first column), for rainfall and runoff from 4 m² (second column), and for rainfall and runoff from 16 m² (third column). In 1975/76, **P** was 560 mm, which results in a T_{act} of 414 mm. In 1973/74, **P** was 430 mm and T_{act} was 314 mm, so *the survival requirement was satisfied* by rainfall only. In 1975/76, T_{act} was already close to the

Table 9.11 Annual rainfall, **P**, and predicted **R**, T_{act}, and **D** (mm) for one Neem tree in a windbreak at *Katsina, Nigeria*, for rainfall only and for rainfall and runoff from 4 m² and 16 m² in different year types.

	Rainfall only	Rainfall and runoff	
Average year		Runoff area 4 m²	Runoff area 16 m²
P (75/76)	560	560	560
R	0	47	185
T_{act}	414	459	595
D	3	1	1
Dry year		Runoff area 4 m²	Runoff area 16 m²
P (73/74)	430	430	430
R	0	35	141
T_{act}	314	347	453
D	0	0	0
Wet year		Runoff area 4 m²	Runoff area 16 m²
P (70/71)	706	706	706
R	0	61	243
T_{act}	402	453	581
D	167	175	229

minimum growth requirement of 450 mm a^{-1}. In the wet year 1970/71, deep percolation of 167 mm occurred from rainfall only.

To achieve minimum growth, a slight increase of T_{act} in 1975/76 is required. The second column shows that, for this, a runoff area of 4 m^2 is already enough. The third column shows that runoff from only 16 m^2 is enough to realize good growth conditions, because T_{act} surpassed the requirement of 450 mm in 1973/74. *In Katsina, good growth is realized* without excessive deep percolation or basin storage problems. In 1970/71, **R** was 243 mm and T_{act} increased to 581 mm. Although **D** is now of the same order as **R**, in absolute terms 229 mm is still acceptable, considering the advantage obtained in a dry year like 1973/74.

The effect of runoff from 16 m^2 on T_{act} in the dry year 1973/74 is shown in Figure 9.10. With rainfall only, the tree takes up water from the soil until the end of the dry season, but at a decreasing rate. With runoff water, good growth is achieved by extending the soil-water uptake period and by increasing T_{act} to a rate that varies from 1.8 to 1.0 mm d^{-1}. Although conditions at Katsina are not extremely dry, and minimum development is almost possible with rainfall only, runoff water clearly

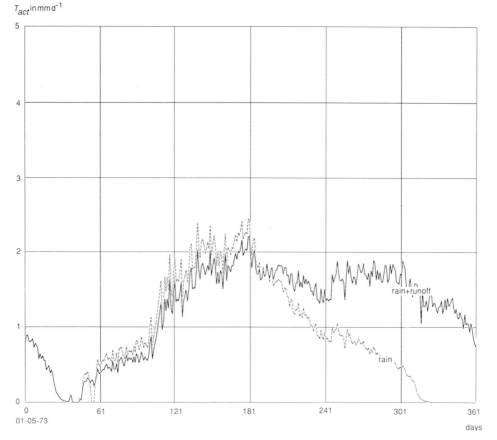

Figure 9.10 SWATRE predicted actual transpiration T_{act} at Katsina, Nigeria, during the dry year 1973/74 for rainfall only and for rainfall supplemented by runoff from 16 m^2.

105

improves tree growth. Because of runoff in 1973/74, T_{act} increased by 44% and good growth was reached.

The deep percolation loss in Table 9.11 is limited compared with Sokoto. This is because P in 1970/71 was 706 mm, whereas in Sokoto the wet year 1952/53 had P equal to 830 mm. Besides, the value of W_{max} in Katsina is different from that in Sokoto. In an average year in Katsina, with runoff from 4 m^2, rooting depth is 4 m and W_{max} is 440 mm. If runoff from 16 m^2 were to be supplied, roots would reach 6 m and W_{max} would be 660 mm. In Sokoto W_{max} was 560 mm.

Conclusion on Micro-Catchment Design at Katsina
The predictions at Katsina indicate that rainfall only is sufficient for Neem trees to survive in the windbreak, and is almost sufficient for them to achieve minimum growth. A runoff area of 4 m^2 is enough to realize this. The runoff area required to achieve good growth conditions completely is only 16 m^2. With a tree spacing of 4 m, this means a 4-m-wide runoff strip for each row of trees. If one considers the advantage this will yield in dry years, and the limited disadvantage of deep percolation and potential basin-storage problems in wet years, *a runoff area of about 16 m^2 is advisable for Katsina.* Values of the achievement ratio, Γ, for Katsina are summarized in Table 9.12.

9.6   Conclusion on Micro-Catchment Design in Niger and Nigeria

Table 9.12 lists the Γ values, calculated from Equation 89, for five locations for which design predictions were made. All values are for Neem trees in a windbreak similar to the experimental windbreak at Sadoré. As is clear from the design predictions discussed earlier, the value Γ reaches at a certain location depends on *rainfall, evaporation, and soil.*

The second column of Table 9.12 shows achievement ratios for *survival conditions.* At all five locations, Neem trees in the windbreak can survive on rainfall only, which is shown by Γ-values of 1.0. The value of 0.9 at Niamey is an exception due to unfavourable rainfall distribution in one particular year.

The third column shows achievement ratios for *minimum growth conditions.* In all locations, Γ is smaller than 1.0 for rainfall only. When runoff is supplied, Γ becomes equal to 1.0. At Tahoua, a runoff area of 40 m^2 is needed to achieve this. In Niamey, Sadoré, and Sokoto, this is achieved with runoff from 20 m^2. The bottom of the table shows that, in Katsina, Γ becomes 1.0 with a runoff area of only 4 m^2. With a tree spacing of 4 m, this would mean a runoff area of 1 m in the flow direction. It would not be practical to construct this in reality, but these dimensions indicate that conditions in Katsina are close to what is needed for minimum growth on rainfall only.

The fourth column shows achievement ratios for *good growth conditions.* With rainfall only, Γ-values are 0.3 for Tahoua, Niamey, and Sadoré, 0.5 for Sokoto, and 0.7 for Katsina. With runoff from larger runoff areas, the Γ-values increase. To achieve good growth conditions, it is critical to consider the dry years, when T_{act} should reach 450 mm a^{-1}. These years determine the required size of the runoff area.

Table 9.12 Achievement ratio, Γ, defined as T_{act}/T_{target} in Equation 89 for rainfall only and for rainfall and runoff from different sizes of runoff area (m²) at Tahoua, Niamey, and Sadoré, in Niger and at Sokoto and Katsina in Nigeria.

	Lower limits for T_{act}		
	Survival *Equations 86a, 86b*	*Minimum growth* *87a, 87b*	*Good growth* *88a, 88b*
T_{act} **(ave year)** $\geq$	**130**	**450**	**450**
T_{act} **(dry year)** $\geq$	130	130	450
Tahoua (Niger)			
Rainfall only	1.0	**0.6**	0.3
Rainfall + Runoff from 40 m²	1.0	**1.0**	**0.6**
Rainfall + Runoff from 80 m²	1.0	1.0	0.8
Rainfall + Runoff from 120 m²	1.0	1.0	1.0
Niamey (Niger)			
Rainfall only	0.9	**0.7**	0.3
Rainfall + Runoff from 20 m²	1.0	**1.0**	**0.4**
Rainfall + Runoff from 40 m²	1.0	1.0	0.6
Sadoré (Niger)			
Rainfall only	1.0	**0.9**	0.3
Rainfall + Runoff from 20 m²	1.0	**1.0**	**0.5**
Rainfall + Runoff from 40 m²	1.0	1.0	0.6
Sokoto (Nigeria)			
Rainfall only	1.0	**0.8**	0.5
Rainfall + Runoff from 20 m²	1.0	**1.0**	**0.8**
Katsina (Nigeria)			
Rainfall only	1.0	**0.9**	0.7
Rainfall + Runoff from 4 m²	1.0	**1.0**	0.8
Rainfall + Runoff from 16 m²	1.0	1.0	**1.0**

Table 9.13 summarizes the rainfall and evaporation data from the five locations. The left side of the table shows P for the years used for the design predictions. The middle section shows average annual rainfall over the period for which daily rainfall

Table 9.13 Annual rainfall, P (mm), at locations in Niger and Nigeria for which data were available and for which design predictions were made in selected dry, average, and wet years. The table also shows the annual average rainfall over the n years period for which data from these locations were available.

Location	P predictions			Annual average P			E_{pan}
	dry	ave	wet	ave	n	period	ave
Tahoua	**219**	344	523	335	13	1972-84	**4215**
Niamey	**230**	466	668	459	13	1970-83	**3380**
Sadoré	**258**	545	673	522	8	1982-89	**3380**
Sokoto	**315**	537	830	536	14	1950-63	**2965**
Katsina	**430**	560	706	552	7	1970-76	**2470**

data were available. The last column shows average annual Class A pan evaporation. For Sadoré, 3380 mm of evaporation was measured. For the other locations, it was estimated as discussed earlier. Moving downwards from the top of the table, which means from north to south and east (Figure 1.5), we find *increasing rainfall and decreasing evaporation.*

In the selected average years (left side of Table 9.13), the value of P is 344 mm at Tahoua, roughly 100 mm higher at Niamey, while at Sadoré, Sokoto, and Katsina, P is about 100 mm higher than at Niamey. This trend is about the same for annual averages (central column). In the dry years, P steadily increases from north to south and east, from 219 mm at Tahoua to 430 mm at Katsina. In the same direction, E_{pan} steadily decreases from 4215 mm at Tahoua to 2470 mm at Katsina. This agrees with the trend for minimum growth shown in Table 9.12. From top to bottom, Γ *reaches 1.0 as the size of the runoff area decreases*: from 40 m² at Tahoua to 4 m² at Katsina.

For an evaluation of Γ values for good growth in the last column of Table 9.12, the soil conditions have to be considered as well. Table 9.14 summarizes the soil texture and depth, the water-holding capacity, $\theta_{FC}-\theta_{WP}$, the depth of the rootzone, $|z_r|$, and the maximum soil water storage, W_{max}. All soils are sandy, but the value of $\theta_{FC}-\theta_{WP}$ varies with texture, and W_{max} varies with rooting depth. Moving from the top of the table towards the bottom, we find that the depth of the rootzone increases from 1.5 m at Tahoua to 6 m at Katsina. This agrees with the trend of increasing rainfall, runoff, and depth of infiltration from Tahoua to Katsina. *From north to south and east, W_{max} increases.*

Although all soils are sandy and of poor quality, the water-holding capacity is better at Tahoua than at the other locations. According to Table 7.2, a reduction in root water uptake starts at pF 2.8. This means that *a portion of the soil water is not readily*

Table 9.14 Staring series soil texture, soil depth (m), water-holding capacity, $\theta_{FC}-\theta_{WP}$, root depth, $|z_r|$ (m), for a given runoff area, A (m²), and maximum soil-water storage of the rootzone, W_{max} (mm), for locations in Niger and Nigeria where design predictions were made.

Location	Staring Series Soil texture	Soil Depth	WHC $\theta_{FC}-\theta_{WP}$	Area A	Root $|z_r|$	Stor W_{max}
Tahoua	Very fine to medium fine sand slightly loamy (Staring 02)	6	0.17	40	1.5	255
Niamey	Very fine to medium fine sand very slightly loamy (Star.01)	3	0.11	20	4.0	400
	Coarse sand, low OM (Star.05)	3	0.07			
Sadoré	Very fine to medium fine sand very slightly loamy (Star.01)	3	0.11	20	5.0	470
	Coarse sand, low OM (Star.05)	3	0.07			
Sokoto	Sokoto slightly loamy sand locally measured $K(\theta)$, $h(\theta)$	3	0.14	20	5.0	560
	Coarse sand, low OM (Star.05)	3	0.07			
Katsina	Very fine to medium fine sand very slightly loamy (Star.01)	6	0.11	16 (4	6.0 4.0	660 440)

is difficult to reach Γ equal to 1.0 for good growth conditions (Table 9.12). Supplying more runoff water increases the depth of infiltration and W_{max}, but not all this water is available. Besides, high hydraulic conductivity causes rapid deep percolation.

Summarizing the Γ values and rainfall and the evaporation and soil data in Tables 9.12, 9.13, and 9.14, we can conclude that, owing to more favourable rainfall and evaporation, *good growth can be reached with runoff from 16 m² at Katsina.* But even without runoff, the achievement ratio Γ is 0.7. In Tahoua, rainfall and evaporation conditions are less favourable, but θ_{FC}-θ_{WP} is higher than at the other locations. With runoff from roughly 40 m², *60% of the requirement for good growth can be reached at Tahoua.* Achieving complete good growth would create basin-storage problems and excessive deep percolation in wet years because of the limited water-holding capacity and high hydraulic conductivity. At the other locations, with runoff from about 20 m², *good growth can be achieved in degrees varying roughly from 40% at Niamey, to 50% at Sadoré, and 80% at Sokoto.*

10 Application: Data Requirement, Summary and Conclusion, Outlook

10.1 Data Requirement for Application

The approach presented in this study can be used to make a *preliminary design* of micro-catchments for rainwater harvesting. In remote regions that are suitable for rainwater harvesting, hydrological data are scarce. Long-term records of rainfall and evaporation are seldom available. Data on surface runoff are usually lacking. Data on soil hydraulic parameters are equally scarce. Under such conditions, drawing up a preliminary design is a problem.

The *hydrological data* required by the runoff models were discussed in Sections 3.3 and 8.1, and the data required to apply SWATRE were dealt with in Sections 7.2 and 8.2. These data are summarized in Table 10.1. The most important data are any available record of weather (daily rainfall, p_1, and daily evaporation, E_{pan}) and data that can be estimated in the field or measured in the laboratory (soil topographic parameters, namely depression storage, d, threshold value, δ, runoff coefficient, ω, and sheet flow velocity, v). Also important are transpiration parameters, $\alpha(h)$, and soil hydraulic parameters, specifically the infiltration rates of dry soil, f_i, and wet soil, f_c, the Horton infiltration constant, a, the saturated and unsaturated hydraulic conductivities, K_s and $K(\theta)$, and the soil water retention characteristic $h(\theta)$.

SWATRE can be applied to the specific conditions prevailing in the area of design. With the results of the soil-water-balance prediction, a preliminary design can be made. After more data have become available, the preliminary design can be adjusted and worked out in detail. Table 10.1 can serve as a framework for the start of micro-catchment design predictions for rainwater harvesting in arid and semi-arid zones with the use of SWATRE.

Table 10.1 Data required for SWATRE-aided design predictions, applied to micro-catchments for Neem windbreaks, as described in Sections 7.2 and 8.1 for an experimental Neem windbreak at Sadoré, Niger.

Type of data or model	Parameters	Table
1) Daily rainfall and evaporation:	P_1, E_{pan}	
2) Root water uptake function $\alpha(h)$:	h_1, h_2, h_3, h_4	Table 7.2
3) Maximum soil-water withdrawal S_{max}:	T_{pot}, $\lvert z_r \rvert$	
4) Factors for ET_0, ET_{pot}, E_{pot}, T_{pot}:	K_{pan}, K_{tree}, K_{soil}	Table 7.3
5) Initial soil-water content:	θ_0	
6) Evaporation of intercepted rain E_i:	P_{av}/E_{av}, C_s, f	Table 7.4
7) Soil hydraulic parameters:	$K(\theta)$, $h(\theta)$	
8) Runoff Depth Model (D) Eq. 52:	ω, δ	Table 8.2
9) Kinematic Wave Model (B) Eq. 35:	d, v, f_i, f_c, a	Table 8.2

10.2   Summary and Conclusion for Application

The objectives of the present study were defined in the Introduction. Models for the inducement and collection of runoff from a defined area have been discussed. Four runoff models were compared as to their concept and structure, their parameters, and their input requirements, and two of the models, the Kinematic Wave Model (B) and the Runoff Depth Model (D), were selected to predict runoff for micro-catchment design. In zones of scarce data, the advantage of Model (D) is the *minimal requirement of input data*.

Rainfall data available for design predictions were very limited, so the Kinematic Wave Model (B) could only be applied at Niamey, in Niger, for a comparison with Runoff Depth Model (D). At all the other locations, Model (D) was used. Nevertheless, the theory and application of Model (B) have been included because Model (B) describes the flow over an infiltrating surface more realistically than Model (D). For future work, it will be important to collect *the data required for the application of the Kinematic Wave Model (B)*.

The 1-D numerical soil-water balance model SWATRE was used to describe the storage and conservation of soil water in the rootzone below a defined basin area. SWATRE was calibrated with data from Sede Boqer in the Negev Desert, and data from the Negev were used for micro-catchment design predictions in two zones: an extremely arid zone with $P < 100$ mm, and an arid zone with *$100 < P < 300$ mm*.

Micro-catchment design was predicted for isolated fruit trees, spaced at 10 to 20 m, growing in a desert and receiving water from rainfall during a cool winter season and from root water uptake during the subsequent dry, hot summer season. The soil in the area was loess with a good water-holding capacity. The rooting depth was about 1 m. The basin area required was unknown. Because the depth of infiltration, deep percolation, and loss of collected water by soil evaporation are all functions of a basin area, the water balance was calculated in m^3. (The application of Equation 4 indicated that extremely arid conditions, with an average annual rainfall of less than 100 mm, are too dry for micro-catchments and require larger catchments.) *For the arid zone, the required basin area was found to be 40 m^2, with a runoff area of between 40 m^2 and 80 m^2.*

To apply SWATRE in the semi-arid zones of Niger and northern Nigeria, where 300 mm $< P < 700$ mm, the model was calibrated with data from an experimental Neem windbreak at Sadoré in Niger. This sub-desert has summer rainfall, followed by a long dry hot season. Soils in the area are deep and sandy with a low water-holding capacity. Neem trees are evergreen, deep-rooting, and drought resistant. From the calibration of SWATRE at Sadoré and the comparison of the Kinematic Wave Model (B) and the Runoff Depth Model (D) at Niamey, *parameter values were set for micro-catchment design predictions*.

Design criteria were developed in terms of lower T_{act} boundaries for survival, minimum development, and good growth of Neem trees in a windbreak. The windbreak design was the same as that of the experimental windbreak at Sadoré: a tree spacing of 4 m, a row distance of 2 m, and a triangular planting pattern. This layout set the basin area at 8 m^2, which left the runoff area to be predicted. With the basin area set, predictions of E_{act} varied less than in the Negev Desert, where E_{act} in m^3 varied with the basin area. Under windbreak conditions, losses varied mainly

112

because of deep percolation. Predictions were made in units of water depth rather than water volume.

Data for design prediction in Niger and Nigeria were available with increasing P from north to south and east (Figure 1.5): from Tahoua (335 mm), Niamey (460 mm), Sadoré (520 mm), Sokoto (535 mm), and Katsina (550 mm). For average, dry, and wet years, T_{act} was calculated. At each location, the driest years were included, which made the lower T_{act} boundary a severe criterion. The probability of exceedance of the selected dry years varied from 90% to 98%, with an average of 93%. The wettest years available were also included. Their probability of exceedance varied from 6% to 18%, with an average of 10%. The degree of realization of the objectives was quantified in a single number *by the definition of the achievement ratio as* $\Gamma = T_{act}/T_{target}$.

At all five locations, Neem trees in the windbreak could survive on rainfall only ($\Gamma = 1.0$). Minimum growth could be realized ($\Gamma = 1.0$), with runoff from areas ranging from 4 m² at Katsina to 40 m² at Tahoua. Good growth could be realized (up to $\approx \Gamma$ 0.5) with runoff from 40 m² (Tahoua) and 20 m² (Niamey and Sadoré). At Sokoto, good growth could be reached (up to $\Gamma = 0.8$), with runoff from 20 m², and at Katsina (up to $\Gamma = 1.0$), with runoff from 16 m².

Table 10.2 summarizes the average Γ values, which show that runoff can not only ensure minimum growth, but it can also increase good growth by more than 50%, to $\Gamma = 0.65$. Because of the assumptions that were made about evaporation, soil hydraulic parameters, and tree characteristics such as water uptake and water requirement, *the findings from these predictions can only be indicative.*

The overall conclusion is that, in arid and semi-arid zones, runoff from such small areas as micro-catchments is an important potential source of water for the establishment, development, and good growth of trees. The supply of runoff water makes the difference between bare survival, minimum development, and good growth. Especially in dry years, the runoff water considerably improves the environmental conditions in which the tree has to grow. From the comparison of the findings from the Negev Desert and the Niger sub-desert, as has been done in this study, three elements appear to be essential:
- *Seasonal distribution of rainfall;*
- *Soil hydraulic conditions;*
- *Tree hydrological characteristics.*

Seasonal Distribution of Rainfall
An important difference between the conditions in the Niger sub-desert and those in the Negev is that, when rainfall and runoff in the Negev are stored in the rootzone,

Table 10.2 General values of the achievement ratio, Γ (Table 9.12), for survival, minimum development, and good growth of a Neem tree in a windbreak in the semi-arid zones of Niger and northern Nigeria.

	Achievement ratio $\Gamma = T_{act}/T_{target}$		
	Survival	Minimum growth	Good growth
Rainfall on 8 m² only	1.0	0.8	0.4
Rainfall on 8 m² plus runoff from 16-40 m²	1.0	1.0	0.65

the trees are inactive and do not take up any water. All the stored soil water is used in the following dry season when the trees become active again and start to take up water. This requires a large storage capacity W_{max}. In Niger, the trees are active throughout the year as long as water is available. As long as rainfall and runoff are stored in the rootzone, the trees are actively taking up water. *From this point of view, Niger conditions are better than Negev conditions.*

Soil Hydraulic Conditions
Rainwater harvesting works best on a soil with a low infiltration rate, which ensures a maximum runoff supply. But it also needs a soil with a high infiltration rate to prevent prolonged waterlogging in the basin area. Owing to these contradictory requirements, a study of soil hydraulic conditions is essential for the selection of an area of application. The loess soil in the Negev Desert forms a surface crust under raindrop impact, which gives a good runoff supply. Bare sandy soils, like those in the Niger sub-desert, also form a crust, but they tend to be less efficient in runoff generation. On sandy soils, *careful preparation of the runoff area is essential.*

To ensure good infiltration in the basin area, the top soil should be broken by tillage before the rainy season starts. At the end of the rainy season, tillage can be repeated to reduce soil evaporation. Besides the soil's infiltration rate, its water-holding capacity has to be considered. Loess soil, for example, has a better water-holding capacity than sandy soil. But, for water harvesting, *the sandy soil has some advantages for the conservation of soil water.*

A low water-holding capacity of a coarse texture causes deep infiltration and deep storage free from evaporation. A coarse soil texture reduces capillary rise to the surface, which adds to the advantage of less soil evaporation. In comparison, finer texture with a high water-holding capacity causes a shallower infiltration and a higher capillary rise. In the Negev, evaporation from the basin area, which is exposed to the sun's rays, was limited, because it occurred during the cool winter season. *Evaporation from an exposed basin area in Niger would be higher.*

A coarse texture, a low water-holding capacity, and a high hydraulic conductivity have, of course, the disadvantage that deep percolation losses increase. In addition, poor sandy soils supply few nutrients to the tree. In a comparative study of sandy soils and loamy soils, loamy soils should still be preferred. They make a runoff supply more efficient, and more runoff means deeper infiltration. This advantage would outweigh the disadvantage of more soil evaporation owing to a high water-holding capacity and capillary rise. Moreover, under windbreak conditions as in Niger, *where the basin is shaded, evaporation is less important.*

Tree Hydrological Characteristics
Tree hydrological characteristics – root uptake, water use, and drought resistance – belong to the third important element in the rainwater-harvesting equation. In the Negev, the basin area needed to maximize W_{max} for a shallow root system was 40 m^2. The Neem tree has the advantage that it grows fast and rapidly develops a deep root system. The low water-holding capacity of the soil and the resulting deep infiltration are compensated for by the roots, which are *capable of taking up this deep soil water.*

The Pistachio tree in the Negev is very drought-resistant. It can live for hundreds

Table 10.3 General values of runoff efficiency, e_R, and water use efficiency, e_U, in the semi-arid zones of Niger and northern Nigeria.

Area	Runoff efficiency $e_R = RB/PA$	Water use efficiency $e_U = T_{act}/I$
Rainfall on 8 m² only	–	0.67
Rainfall on 8 m² plus runoff from 16-40 m²	0.16	0.72

of years, but is slow in its growth. The trees used developed a 1-m-deep root system, and soil-water storage below this depth is lost to deep percolation. Selecting the right type of tree for the prevailing conditions is a vital matter. A tree suitable for rainwater harvesting is *drought-resistant with a root system that grows fast and deep.*

Efficiencies of Runoff, e_R, and Water Use, e_U

Water-use efficiencies, e_u, as defined by Boers et al. (1986a) and Equation 84, were calculated in all cases of application. The total quantities of infiltrated water are subject to annual evaporation and percolation losses. These losses, in turn, depend on rainfall and runoff distribution, soil hydraulic conditions, and tree hydrological characteristics. Table 10.3 shows general values of e_U for rainfall only and for rainfall plus runoff. A general runoff efficiency value is also given.

If forced to survive on rainfall only, the tree uses the scarce water efficiently, which is expressed in the high value of 0.67 for e_U. The problem is that, on rainfall only, T_{act} remains low, resulting in a low achievement ratio for good growth (Table 10.2). Runoff in addition to rainfall increases e_U to 0.72, owing to the deep storage of soil water. The runoff efficiency, e_R, is low (0.16) because of the natural soil condition of the runoff area. An increase in e_R would mean that T_{act} could be increased with a smaller runoff area. But, as was discussed in Section 1.4, methods to increase e_R with chemicals have not been studied. Besides, land was not considered the main limiting factor in these marginal, dry lands.

A value of 0.72 for e_U can be attained through the construction of a low-cost strip of runoff areas adjacent to a windbreak. This will increase the good growth of trees considerably. A comparison with irrigated agriculture shows that this efficiency is not bad, the average irrigation project efficiency being 0.40 (Wolters 1992). The e_U value of 0.72 also compares well with the field application efficiency in irrigated agriculture, which varies from 0.53 to 0.63 (Wolters 1992). The comparison is even more favourable for rainwater harvesting because field application efficiency is based on ET_{act}, whereas e_U is based on T_{act}. This comparison shows that *rainwater harvesting is an efficient method of using scarce desert rainfall.*

The only alternative method of water supply to a windbreak would be trickle irrigation. Nevertheless, this would enhance the development of a shallow root system and require a source of water, high capital investment, and irrigation management skills. All of these requirements are difficult to realize in a windbreak application. For windbreaks, rainwater harvesting from micro-catchments is *suitable, cheap, good, and efficient.*

The comparison between rainwater harvesting and irrigated agriculture shows that these practices are complementary rather than competitive. Irrigated agriculture is usually practised on the best soils, where water is available to grow field crops. Rainwater harvesting is a good possibility on marginal soils, where irrigation water is not available. Because of dry periods and drought years, rainwater harvesting works best for *deep-rooting, drought-resistant trees.*

10.3   Outlook for Application

Rainwater harvesting should suit its purpose, be accepted by the local population, and be good for the environment. Field crops with shallow roots fail in dry years, which does not inspire people's confidence in the system. Deep-rooting and drought-resistant *trees constitute the most promising application.*

The low runoff efficiencies of natural surfaces make rainwater harvesting an extensive practice, requiring extra land for the runoff strips. Since, in most areas, the best soils are used for field crops, typical locations where rainwater harvesting is applied are *marginal soils, especially those on the desert fringes.*

Rainwater harvesting technology is not complicated and can easily be adapted to local conditions of climate, soil, and trees. In many areas of potential application there is a lack of water, wood, food, and shade, and wind erosion is a major problem. This study concentrated on rainwater harvesting to supply water to windbreaks. But rainwater harvesting can also be used to establish *shelterbelts, many of which have been planted in Niger and Nigeria.*

As mentioned earlier, the European Union is supporting the Government of Nigeria in implementing three large rural development programmes in the northern states of Sokoto, Katsina, and Borno. Although rainwater harvesting is not being applied there, it could be considered. In Katsina, for instance, windbreaks and shelterbelts have been established, and windbreaks are popular with the local farmers. *They serve both the local population and the environment.*

An important characteristic of rainwater harvesting for trees is that micro-catchments do not require intensive farming or maintenance. Once the trees have been planted and the runoff areas have been constructed, the system only needs some annual maintenance. This is important for nomads, who are not farmers. Windbreaks can be designed specifically to protect farm land and be maintained by farmers. Large-scale shelterbelts would serve nomads, who do not settle but *move with their camels through the desert in search of water, food, grass, wood, and shelter.*

Windbreaks and Shelterbelts
A typical windbreak of 150 m consists of a hundred trees, planted in a double row, and covering 450 m² (Figure 10.1). A shelterbelt is a long strip of trees and bushes, planted at a right angle to the direction of the prevailing dry season wind (Figure 10.2). A shelterbelt is normally planted in a series comprising several shelterbelts 200 m apart. Each shelterbelt is 2 km long and 30 m wide. When mature, they will provide considerable protection for the surrounding land. They are also a valuable source of forest produce from thinnings. Shelterbelts are intended to reduce wind erosion of the top soil and to stabilize sand in areas already suffering from the effects of desertification (Hedeselskabet 1990; Ujah and Adeoye 1984).

Whereas a windbreak consists of one type of tree, a shelterbelt can consist of

116

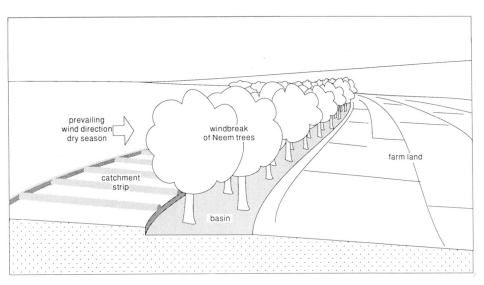

Figure 10.1 Windbreak built in a double row with about one hundred trees. Catchment strip on upslope side supplies runoff water which collects in the basin area. The windbreak is used to demarcate farmland and to protect the land against wind erosion.

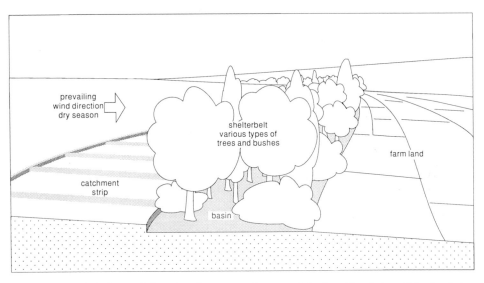

Figure 10.2 Shelterbelt, consisting of various types of trees and bushes. The design of the bordering catchment strip is adjusted to the water requirement of the trees. The shelterbelt protects the environment against desert wind, provides shelter for man and animals, and produces firewood from thinnings.

different types of trees and bushes that have different requirements. Tree spacing, row distance, and planting pattern can thus vary, and so, too, can the micro-catchment design. Usually, seedlings from a nursery are transplanted and then given some water from a tanker. But after this, they have to survive on rainfall only, which causes a

117

certain mortality. Rainwater harvesting can be used to speed up tree establishment and deep root development, and will *reduce the mortality rate*.

The trees in windbreaks and shelterbelts serve the population by demarcating farms, protecting field crops, reducing wind erosion of farm soils, and providing firewood and shade. At the same time, the micro-catchments reduce soil erosion by water because they control the surface flow, while deep percolation recharges the groundwater. This can help to redress an upset regional water balance. In this study, the Neem tree was taken as an example, but many other kinds of trees (e.g. *Acacia albida* and *Eucalyptus camaldulensis*) can be used to *conserve the environment and improve conditions in desert fringes*.

References

Aldon, E.F. and H.W. Springfield 1975. Using paraffin and polyethylene to harvest water for growing shrubs. In: *Proc. Water Harvesting Symp., Phoenix, AZ*, ARS W-22, USDA, pp. 251-257.

Amerman, C.R. and J.L. McGuinness 1968. Plot and small watershed runoff: Its relation to larger areas. In: *Trans. ASAE*, 10(4): 464-466.

Anaya, M.G. and J.S. Tovar 1975. Different soil treatments for harvesting water for radish production in the Mexico Valley. In: *Proc. Water Harvesting Symp., Phoenix, AZ*, ARS W-22, USDA, pp. 315-320.

Beldt, R.J. van den 1989. Agroforestry in the Semi-Arid Tropics: Strategies and Research Needs. In: ICRISAT 1989. *Soil, Crop and Water Management Systems for Rain-Fed Agriculture in the Sudano-Sahelian Zone. Proc. Int. Workshop 7-11 Jan. 1987.* ICRISAT Sahelian Centre/ISC, Niamey, Niger.

Belmans, C., J.G. Wesseling, and R.A. Feddes 1983. Simulation model of the water balance of a cropped soil: SWATRE. In: *J. Hydrol.* 63: 271-286.

Benge, M.D. 1988. Cultivation and propagation of the Neem tree. In: Jacobson, M. (Ed.). *Phytochemical Pesticides, Vol.1: The Neem Tree*. CRC Press Inc., Boca Raton, FL, U.S.A.

Black, T.A., W.R. Gardner, and G.W. Thurtell 1969. The prediction of evaporation, drainage and soil water storage for a bare soil. In: *Soil Sci. Soc. Am. Proc.* 33: 655-660.

Bloemen, G.W. 1980. Calculation of hydraulic conductivities from texture and organic matter content. In: *Z. Pflanzenernaehr. Bodenkd.*, 143(5): 581-605 (Winand Staring Centre, Tech. Bull. 120).

Boers, Th.M. and J. Ben-Asher 1980. Harvesting water in the desert. In: *Annual Report 1979*, International Institute for Land Reclamation and Improvement, Wageningen, Netherlands, pp. 6-23.

Boers, Th.M. and J. Ben-Asher 1982. A review of rainwater harvesting. In: *Agric. Water Management* 5: 145-158.

Boers, Th.M., M. de Graaf, R.A. Feddes, and J. Ben-Asher 1986a. A linear regression model combined with a soil water balance model to design micro-catchments for water harvesting in arid zones. In: *Agric. Water Management* 11: 187-206.

Boers, Th.M., J. Zondervan, and J. Ben-Asher 1986b. Micro-Catchment-Water-Harvesting (MCWH) for arid zone development. In: *Agric. Water Management* 12: 21-39.

Boers, Th.M., H.O. Maduakor, and D.P. Tee 1988. Sheet erosion from a bare sandy soil in South Eastern Nigeria. In: Ijioma, C.I. (Chief Editor) *Proc. Int. Symp. on Erosion in SE Nigeria, at the Federal University of Technology, Owerri, Nigeria* (1)1: 23-34.

Boers, Th.M. 1990. Better infiltration measurements with new rainfall simulator. In: *Landbouwkundig Tijdschrift* 102(4): 21-22.

Boers, Th.M., W.H. van der Molen, L.A. Eppink, and J. Ben-Asher 1991. Effect of Thomson weir and weirbox on measurement of flow rates from micro-catchments and runoff plots. In: *J. Hydrol.* 128: 29-39.

Boers, Th.M., F.J. van Deurzen, L.A. Eppink, and R.E. Ruytenberg 1992. Comparison of infiltration rates measured with an infiltrometer a rainulator and a permeameter. In: *Soil. Tech.* (5): 13-26.

Boers, Th.M., H.J. van Ieperen, P.J. Torfs, and J. Ben-Asher 1994. Kinematic wave solution for runoff from a plane subject to rainfall and infiltration. In: *J. Hydrol.* 23 pp. (Accepted).

Bognetteau-Verlinden, E. 1980. *Study on the impact of windbreaks in the Majia Valley, Niger*. M.Sc. Thesis, Wageningen Agric. Univ., The Netherlands, 88 pp.

Brenner, A.J., P.G. Jarvis, and R.J. Vandenbeldt 1991. Transpiration from a Neem windbreak in the Sahel. In: *Proc. Niamey Workshop Feb. 1991: Soil Water Balance in the Sudano-Sahelian Zone*. IAHS Publ. No. 199: 375-385.

Burdass, W.J. 1975. Water harvesting for livestock in Western Australia. In: *Proc. Water Harvesting Symp., Phoenix, AZ*, ARS W-22, USDA, pp. 8-26.

Burden, R.L., J. Douglas-Faires, and A.C. Reynolds 1978. *Numerical Analysis*. Prindle, Weber & Schmidt, Boston, MA. 598 pp.

Campbell, S.Y., W.H. van der Molen, C.W. Rose and J.Y. Parlange 1985. A new method for obtaining a spatially averaged infiltration rate from rainfall and runoff rates. *J. Hydrol*, 82: 57-68.

Chiarella, J.V. and W.H. Beck, W.H. 1975. Water harvesting catchments on Indian lands in the Southwest. In: *Proc. Water Harvesting Symp., Phoenix, AZ*, ARS W-22, USDA, pp. 104-114.

Cluff, C.B. 1979. The use of the compartmented reservoir in water harvesting agrisystems. In: Goodin, J.R. and D.K. Northington (Editors) *Arid Land Plant Resources*. Texas Technical University, Lubbock, TX, pp. 482-500.

Cooley, K.R., A.R. Dedrick, and G.W. Frasier 1975. Water harvesting: State of the art. Reprinted from: *Watershed Management Symp.* ASCE Irr. Drain. Div., Logan, UT, 20 pp.

Dan, J., R. Moshe, and N. Alperovitch 1973. The soils of Sede Zin. In: *Israel Journal of Earth Sciences* 22: 211-227.

De Jussieu, A. 1963. Azadirachta indica and Melia azedarach Linne: Silvicultural characteristics and planting methods. In: *Rev. Bois Forest Trop.* 88(23).

Diskin, M.H. 1970. Definition and uses of the linear regression model. In: *Water Resour. Res.* 6: 1668-1673.

Diskin, M.H., N. Buras, and S. Zamir 1973. Application of a simple hydrologic model for rainfall-runoff relations of the Dalton Watershed. In: *Water Resour. Res.* 9: 927-936.

Doorenbos, J., and W.O. Pruitt 1977. *Crop Water Requirements*. FAO Irrigation and Drainage Paper No. 24. FAO, Rome, 144 pp.

Ehrler, W.L., D.H. Fink, and S.T. Mitchell 1978. Growth and yield of Jojoba plants in native stands using runoff-collecting micro-catchments. In: *Agron. J.* 70: 1005-1009.

Evenari, M., L. Shanan, and N.H. Tadmor 1968. Runoff farming in the desert. I. Experimental layout. In: *Agron. J.* 60: 29-32.

Evenari, M., L. Shanan, and N.H. Tadmor 1971. *The Negev: The Challenge of a Desert*. Harvard University Press, Cambridge, MA, 345 pp.

Fairbourn, M.L. 1975. Field evaluation of microwatershed and vertical mulch systems. In: *Proc. Water Harvesting Symp., Phoenix, AZ*, ARS W-22, USDA, pp. 233-243.

FAO 1974. *Tree planting practices in African savannas*. Food and Agriculture Organization of the United Nations, Forestry Development Paper No. 19, Rome.

FAO 1989. *Arid zone forestry*. Food and Agriculture Organization of the United Nations, FAO Conservation Guide 20, Rome, 143 pp.

Feddes, R.A. 1971. *Water, Heat and Crop Growth*. Veenman, Wageningen, The Netherlands, 184 pp.

Feddes, R.A., P.J. Kowalik, and H. Zaradny 1978. Simulation of field water use and crop yield. In: *Simul. Monogr.*, Pudoc, Wageningen, 189 pp.

Fink, D.H. 1976. Laboratory testing of water-repellent soil treatments for water harvesting. In: *Soil Sci. Soc. Am. J.* 40: 562-566.

Fink, D.H., G.W. Frasier, and L.E. Myers 1979. Water harvesting treatment evaluation at Granite Reef. In: *Water Res. Bull.* 15: 861-873.

Fishwick, R.W. 1970. Sahel and Sudan zone of northern Nigeria, North Cameroon and the Sudan. In: Kaul, R.N. (Ed.). *Afforestation in Arid Zones*. Dr. W. Junk N.V. Publ., The Hague, The Netherlands.

Fowler, W.P. and P.F. Ffolliott 1986. An agroforestry demonstration in the Avra Valley of southeastern Arizona. In: *Hydrology and Water Resources in Arizona and the Southwest* 16: 1-10.

Frasier, G.W., G.R. Dutt, and D.H. Fink 1987. Sodium salt treated catchments for water harvesting. In: *Transact. ASAE* 30(3): 658-664.

Frith, J.L. 1975. Design and construction of roaded catchments. In: *Proc. Water Harvesting Symp., Phoenix, AZ*, ARS W-22, USDA, pp. 122-127.

Gardner, H.R. 1975. An analysis of the efficiency of microwatershed systems. In: *Proc. Water Harvesting Symp., Phoenix, AZ*, ARS W-22. USDA, pp. 244-250.

Gash, J.H.C. 1979. An analytical model of rainfall interception by forests. In: *Quart. J. R. Met. Soc.* 105: 43-55.

Gregory, P.J. 1984. Water availability and crop growth in arid regions. In: *Outlook on Agric.* 13(4): 208-215.

Haskoning 1991. Personal communication. Nijmegen, The Netherlands.

Hedeselskabet 1990. Katsina Afforestation Project, Federal Government of Nigeria, European Economic Community. Danish Land Development Service Hedeselskabet. *Brief information on the project*. No. 6, 6 pp.

Henderson, F.M. and R.A. Wooding 1964. Overland flow and groundwater flow from a steady rainfall of finite duration. In: *J. Geophysical Research* 69(8): 1531-1540.

Hendriks, M.J., P. Kabat, J. Homma, and J. Postma 1990. *Research on evapotranspiration of a forest. Measured data and model calculations*. Report 90, Winand Staring Centre, Wageningen, the Netherlands (In Dutch).

Hillel, D. 1967. *Runoff inducement in arid lands*. Final Technical Report submitted to USDA. Volcani Institute of Agricultural Research and Hebrew University of Jerusalem, Faculty of Agriculture, Rehovot, Israel, 142 pp.

Hoogmoed, W.B. 1981. Field experiments on infiltration, runoff, tillage and millet emergence in Mali. In: Rawitz, E., W.B. Hoogmoed, and Y. Morin (Eds.) *Development of criteria and methods for improving the efficiency of soil management and tillage operations with special reference to arid and semi-arid regions.* Hebrew Univ., Dept. of Soil and Water Science, Rehovot, Israel, and Wageningen Agric. Univ., Soil Tillage Lab., Wageningen, The Netherlands, App. 3, 37 pp.

Hoogmoed, W.B. 1985. Crusting and sealing problems on West African soils. In: *Proc. Int. Symp. on the assessment of soil surface sealing and crusting.* Ghent, Belgium, pp. 48-55.

Hoogmoed, W.B. 1987. Some aspects of crust formation on soils in semi-arid regions. In: *Proc. Consultants Workshop on State of the Art and Management Alternatives for Optimizing the Productivity of SAT Alfisols and Related Soils.* ICRISAT Centre, Patancheru, India, pp. 127-135.

Hoogmoed, W. 1991. Personal Communication. Wageningen Agric. Univ., Dept. of Soil Tillage, Wageningen, The Netherlands.

Hoogmoed, W.B. and L. Stroosnijder 1984. Crust formation on sandy soils in the Sahel. I. Rainfall and infiltration. In: *Soil & Tillage Research* 4: 5-23.

Hoogmoed, W.B. and M.C. Klaij 1990. Soil management for crop production in the West African Sahel. I. Soil and climate parameters. In: *Soil & Tillage Research* 16: 85-103.

Hoover, J.R. 1975. Precipitation entrapment for evaporation suppression. In: *Proc. Water Harvesting Symp., Phoenix, AZ,* ARS W-22, USDA, pp.259-268.

Horton, R.E. 1939. Analysis of runoff-plat experiments with varying infiltration capacity. In: *Trans. American Geophys. Union. Reports & Papers, Hydrology*: 693-711.

Israelsen, O.W. and V.E. Hansen 1962. *Irrigation Principles and Practices.* J. Wiley & Sons, New York, NY, p. 292.

Karnieli, A. and J. Ben-Asher 1993. A daily runoff simulation in semi-arid watersheds based on soil water deficit calculations. In: *J. Hydrol.* 149: 9-25.

Ketkar, C.M. 1976. *Utilization of Neem (Azadirachta indica juss) and its by-products.* Report of the Modified Neem Cake Manurial Project 1969-1976.

Lal, R., 1983. Effects of slope length on runoff from alfisols in Western Nigeria. In: *Geoderma* 31: 185-193.

Latum, E.B.J. van 1985. The Neem tree in agriculture, its uses in low-input pest management. In: *Ecoscript 31.* Foundation for Ecological Development Alternatives, Zandvoort, The Netherlands.

Lighthill, M.J. and G.B. Witham 1955a. On kinematic waves, I. Flood movement in long rivers. In: *Proc. Roy. Soc. London,* Vol. 229 A: 281-316.

Lighthill, M.J. and G.B. Witham 1955b. On kinematic waves, II. A theory of traffic flow on long crowded roads. In: Proc. Roy. Soc. London, Vol. 229 A: 317-345.

Lima, J.L.M.P. de 1989. *Overland flow under rainfall: Some aspects related to modelling and conditioning factors.* Doctoral Thesis, Wageningen Agric. Univ. The Netherlands, 160 pp.

Lima, J.L.M.P. de and P.J.J.F. Torfs 1990. Upper boundary conditions for overland flow. In: *J. Hydraul. Eng.* 116(7): 951-957.

Linsley, R.K., M.A. Kohler, and J.L.H. Paulhus 1982. *Hydrology for Engineers.* McGraw-Hill, Japan, 508 pp.

Long, S.P. and N. Persaud 1988. Influence of Neem (Azadirachta Indica) windbreaks on millet yield, micro-climate and water use in Niger, West Africa. In: *Challenges in Dryland Agriculture: A Global Perspective. Proc. Int. Conf. on Dryland Farming, Amarillo/Bushland, Texas, August 1988.* Texas A&M University Press, College Station, TX, pp.313-314.

Lou, M.Y., B.X. Zheng, Q. Zhu, C. Gao, F.X. Wu, S.Q. Zhang, and Y.Z. Jin 1991. Experiments on rainfall collection and its utilization in the arid area of Gansu Province, China. In: *Proc. ICID Special Technical Session, Vol.1-B Operation of Irrigation Systems,* Beijing, China, pp. 245-253.

Lövenstein, H.M., P.R. Berliner, and H. van Keulen 1991. Runoff agroforestry in arid lands. In: *For. Ecol. Manage.* 45: 59-70.

MacDonald Agricultural Services 1991. Personal communication, Cambridge, England.

Madougou, Z., A. Solheim, D. Steinberg, and R.M. Rochette 1987. Le Brise-vent de la Maggia et de Maiguizaoua, Tahoua/Maradi/Niger; Brise-vent et agroforesterie rurale. In: Rochette, R.M. (Ed.) *Le Sahel en Lutte contre la Désertification; Leçons d'Expériences.* CILSS, Weikersheim: Margraf, 1989.

Moore, I.D. and P.I.A. Kinnell 1987. Kinematic overland flow: Generalization of Rose's approximate solution, II. In: *J. Hydrol.* 92: 351-362.

Morin, J. and Benyamini 1977. Rainfall infiltration into bare soils. In: *Water Resour. Res.* 13: 813-817.

Morris, M., and O.E. Brown 1964. *Differential equations.* Prentice-Hall, Englewood cliffs, New Jersey, 4th ed., 366 pp.

121

Morris, E.M. and D.A. Woolhiser 1980. Unsteady one-dimensional flow over a plane: Partial equilibrium and recession hydrographs. In: *Water Resour. Res.* 16: 355-360.

Mulder, J.P.M. 1985. Simulation interception loss using standard meteorological data. In: Hutchinson, B.A. and B.B. Hicks (Eds.) *The Forest-Atmosphere Interaction*, pp. 177-196.

Myers, L.E. 1964. Harvesting precipitation. In: IASH Publ. 65. *Land Erosion, Precipitations, Hydrometry, Soil Moisture*, pp. 343-351.

Myers, L.E. 1967. Recent advances in water harvesting. In: *J. Soil Water Conserv.* 22: 95-97.

Myers, L.E. 1975. Water harvesting 2000 B.C. to 1974 A.D. In: *Proc. Water Harvesting Symp., Phoenix, AZ*, ARS W-22, USDA, pp. 1-7.

National Academy of Sciences 1974. *More water for arid lands*. Nat. Acad. of Sci. Washington DC, 154 pp.

National Academy of Sciences 1980. *Firewood Crops: shrub and tree species for energy production*. Nat. Acad. Sci., Washington, D.C.

Ngatunga, E.L.N., R. Lal, and A.P. Uriyo 1984. Effects of surface management on runoff and soil erosion from some plots at Mlingano, Tanzania. In: *Geoderma* 33: 1-12.

Obi, M.E., 1982. Runoff and soil loss from an oxisol in southeastern Nigeria under various management practices. In: *Agric. Water Manage.* 5: 193-203.

Overton, D.E., 1974. Simulating overland flow on hillslopes with a kinematic cascade. In: *Proc. Warsaw Symp. July 1971 on Mathematical models in hydrology*. IAHS Publ. 101, p. 784.

Overton, D.E. and M.E. Meadows 1976. *Stormwater Modelling*. Academic Press, New York, NY, 358 pp.

Parlange, J.Y., C.W. Rose, and G. Sander 1981. Kinematic flow approximation of runoff on a plane: An exact analytical solution. In: *J. Hydrol.* 52: 171-176.

Pepper, R.G. and J.G. Morrissey 1985. Soil properties affecting runoff. In: *J. Hydrol.* 79: 301-310.

Porto, E.R., A. de S. Silva, L.T. de L. Brito, and M.A.R. Monteiro 1989. In situ rainwater harvesting. II. Stand density in cowpea. In: *Arido* 35: 25-37.

Prasad, R. 1988. A linear root water uptake model. In: *J. Hydrol.* 99: 297-306.

Radwanski, S.A. 1980. Multiple land use in the tropics: An integrated approach with proposals for an International Neem Tree Research and Development Program. In: *Proc. 1st. Int. Neem Conf.*, Rottach-Egern, pp. 267-278.

Rauzi, F., M.L. Fairbourn, and L. Landers 1973. Water harvesting efficiencies of four soil surface treatments. In: *J. Range Manage.*, 26: 399-403.

Rawitz, E. and D. Hillel 1975. Water harvesting by runoff inducement for irrigation of an almond orchard in a semi-arid climate. In: *Proc. Water Harvesting Symp., Phoenix, AZ*, ARS W-22, USDA, pp. 223-232.

Ritchie, K.A. 1988. Shelterbelt plantings in semi-arid areas. In: *Agric. Ecosystems Environ.* 22/23: 425-440.

Rutter, A.J., K.A. Kershaw, P.C. Robins, and A.J. Morton 1971. A predictive model of rainfall interception in forests. 1. Derivation of the model from observations in a plantation of Corsican pine. In: *Agric. Meteorol.* 9: 367-384.

Rutter, A.J., P.C. Robins, and A.J. Morton 1975. A predictive model of rainfall interception in forests. 2. Generalization of the model and comparison with observations in some coniferous and hardwood stands. In: *J. Appl. Ecol.* 12: 367-380.

Sharma, K.D. 1986. Runoff behaviour of water harvesting microcatchments. In: *Agric. Water Manage.* 11(2): 137-144.

Sharma, K.D., O.P. Pareek, and H.P. Singh 1982. Effect of runoff concentration on growth and yield of Jujube. In: *Agric. Water Manage.* 5: 73-84.

Sharma, K.D., O.P. Pareek, and H.P. Singh 1986. Microcatchment water harvesting for raising jujube orchards in an arid climate. In: *Transact. ASAE* 29(1): 112-118.

Singh, V.P. 1978. Mathematical modelling of watershed runoff. In: *Proc. Int. Conf. Water Resour. Eng.*, Asian Institute of Technology, Vol.II: 703-726.

Sivakumar, M.V.K., S.M. Virmani, and S.J. Reddy 1979. *Rainfall Climatology of West Africa: Niger*. ICRISAT Information Bull. No. 5, Patancheru P.O. Andhra Pradesh, India 502 324, 66 pp.

Smith, G.L. 1978. *Water Harvesting Technology Applicable to Semi-Arid Subtropical Climates*. Colorado State University, Fort Collins, CO, U.S.A., 95 pp.

Smith, R.E. and R.H.B. Hebbert 1983. Mathematical simulation of interdependent surface and subsurface hydrologic processes. In: *Water Resour. Res.* (19)4: 987-1001.

Spiegel-Roy, P., D. Mazigh, and M. Evenari 1977. Response of pistachio to low soil moisture conditions. In: *J. Am. Hortic. Sci.* 102: 470-473.

Stephenson, D. and M.E. Meadows 1986. *Kinematic Hydrology and Modelling*. Development in Water Science, 26. Elsevier Science Publishers, Amsterdam, 250 pp.

Ujah, J.E. and K.B. Adeoye 1984. Effects of shelterbelts in the Sudan savanna zone of Nigeria on microclimate and yield of millet. In: *Agric. For. Meteorol*. 33: 99-107.

United Nations 1977. *Desertification: Its Causes and Consequences*. Secretariat of the U.N. Conference on Desertification, Nairobi. Pergamon Press, Oxford.

Verhoef, A and R.A. Feddes 1991. Personal Communication. Wageningen Agric. Univ., Dept. of Meteorology, Wageningen, The Netherlands.

Vieira, J.H.D. 1983. Conditions governing the use of approximations for the Saint-Venant equations for shallow surface water flow. In: *J. Hydrol*. 60: 43-58.

Vittal, K.P.R., K. Vijayalakshmi, and U.M.B. Rao 1989. Interception and storage of surface runoff in ponds in small agricultural watersheds, Andhra Pradesh, India. In: *Irrigation Science* 9(1): 69-75.

Wesseling, J.G., G.W. Bloemen, and W.A.J.M. Kroonen 1984. *Computer program "CAPSEV" to calculate: I, Soil hydraulic conductivity from grain size distribution. II, Steady state water flow in layered soil profiles*. Nota 1500, Winand Staring Centre, Wageningen, The Netherlands, 34 pp.

Wesseling, J.G., P. Kabat, B.J. van den Broek, and R.A. Feddes 1989. *SWACROP. An instruction for input*. Winand Staring Centre for Integrated Land, Soil, and Water Research, P.O. Box 125, 6700 AA Wageningen, The Netherlands, 29 pp.

West, L.T., L.P. Wilding, J.K. Landeck, and F.G. Calhoun 1984. *Soil Survey of the ICRISAT Sahelian Centre, Niger, West Africa*. Soil and Crop Sciences Dept./Trop Soils, Texas A&M University System, College Station, TX, 66 pp.

Wit, K.E. 1967. Apparatus for measuring hydraulic conductivity of undisturbed soil samples. Reprinted from: *Permeability and Capillarity of Soils*, Spec. Tech. Publ. 417, American Society for Testing and Materials, Philadelphia, PA, pp. 72-83 (Winand Staring Centre, Tech. Bull. 52).

Wolters, W. 1992. Influences on the efficiency of irrigation water use. Ph. D. dissertation Delft, University of Technology. ILRI Publication 51, Wageningen, The Netherlands, 150 pp.

Woolhiser, D.A. and J.A. Liggett 1967. Unsteady one-dimensional flow over a plane: The rising hydrograph. In: *Water Resour. Res*. 3(3): 753-771.

Wösten, J.H.M. 1987. *Description of the soil water retention and hydraulic conductivity characteristics from the Staring Series with analytical functions*. Winand Staring Centre, Wageningen, The Netherlands, STI Report 2019, 53 pp. (In Dutch).

Wösten, J.H.M., M.H. Bannink, and J. Beuving 1987. *Soil-water retention and hydraulic conductivity characteristics of top soils and sub-soils in The Netherlands: The Staring Series*. Winand Staring Centre, Wageningen, The Netherlands, STI Report 1932, ICW Report 18, 75 pp. (In Dutch).

Yair, A. and A. Danin 1980. Spatial variations in vegetation as related to the soil moisture regime over an arid limestone hillside, Northern Negev, Israel. In: *Oecologia* (Berlin) 47: 83-88.

Yeomans, P.A. 1965. *Water for every farm*. Murray Publishing Co. Ltd., Sidney, Australia, 237 pp.

Zarmi, Y., J. Ben-Asher, and Th. Greengard 1983. Constant velocity kinematic analysis of an infiltrating micro-catchment hydrograph. In: *Water Resour. Res*. (19)1: 277-283.

123

Appendices

A.1 Analytical Solution of the Kinematic-Wave-Equation with Depression Storage by the Laplace Transformation

The Rising Hydrograph

Equations 15 and 34, subject to Equation 32, are solved by first applying the Laplace transformation with respect to T:

$$D^*(s,x) = L_s\{D(s,x)\} = \int_0^\infty e^{-sT} D(T,x) \, dT \tag{1}$$

For the transformed Equations 15 and 34, the standard transformations for $L\{A\}$, $L\{e^{ax}\}$, $L\{f'(x)\}$ (Morris and Brown, 1964), and Equation 32a give:

$$dD^*/dx + (s/v)D^* = A/vs - C/v(s+a) \tag{2}$$

Multiplication of (2) by the integrating factor, $e^{sx/v}$, gives:

$$dD^*/dx \, e^{sx/v} + (s/v)D^* \, e^{sx/v} = (A/vs)e^{sx/v} - [C/v(s+a)]e^{sx/v} \tag{3}$$

For D^*, integration of (3) and subsequent multiplication by $e^{-sx/v}$ gives:

$$D^* = A/s^2 - C/s(s+a) + F e^{-sx/v} \tag{4}$$

The constant of integration F follows from Equation 32b; (4) becomes:

$$D^* = A/s^2 - C/s(s+a) - (A/s^2)e^{-sx/v} + [C/s(s+a)]e^{-sx/v} \tag{5}$$

The solution in D is found from (5) by applying: $L^{-1}\{1/s^2\}$, $L^{-1}\{1/s(s+a)\}$, $L^{-1}\{(1/s^2)e^{-sx/v}\}$ and $L^{-1}\{[1/s(s+a)]e^{-sx/v}\}$:

$$D(x,T) = AT - (C/a)[1 - e^{-aT}] \text{ for } T < x/v \tag{6a}$$

$$D(x,T) = A(x/v) - (C/a)[e^{-a(T-x/v)} - e^{-aT}] \text{ for } T > x/v \tag{6b}$$

The Recession Curve

If, at $t = 0$, it is assumed that $P = 0, f = f_c$, and that steady state exists, Equations 15 and 34 become:

$$\partial D/\partial t + v \, \partial D/\partial x = -f_c \tag{7}$$

$$\text{At } t = 0, \text{ steady state exists: } q = vD = Ax \tag{8}$$

With $E = A/v$, (8) becomes:

$$D = q/v = Ax/v = Ex \tag{9}$$

The following conditions apply:

Initial condition (steady state): $D = Ex, x > 0, t = 0$ (10a)

Boundary condition (dry top): $D = 0, x = 0, t \geq 0$ (10b)

125

With the standard transformations, (7) becomes:

$$v \, dD^*/dx + sD^* = Ex - f_c/s \tag{11}$$

If this is divided by v and multiplied by the integrating factor, $e^{sx/v}$:

$$dD^*/dx \, e^{sx/v} + (s/v)D^* \, e^{sx/v} = (Ex/v) \, e^{sx/v} - (f_c/sv) \, e^{sx/v} \tag{12}$$

If (12) is integrated and multiplied by $e^{-sx/v}$, it gives:

$$D^* = Ex/s - Ev/s^2 - f_c/s^2 + G \, e^{-sx/v} \tag{13}$$

The constant of integration, G, follows from (10b); (13) becomes:

$$D^* = Ex/s - Ev/s^2 - f_c/s^2 + [(Ev+f_c)/s^2]e^{-sx/v} \tag{14}$$

This is the solution to (11). If $L^{-1}\{1/s\}$, $L^{-1}\{1/s^2\}$,
and $L^{-1}\{e^{-sx/v}\}$ are applied, the original solution to (7) is:

$$D(x,t) = Ex - (Ev+f_c)t + (Ev+f_c)(t-x/v) \, U(t-x/v) \tag{15}$$

For small t: $U = 0$ and (15) becomes:

$$D(x,t) = Ex - (Ev+f_c)t \tag{16}$$

This satisfies (11) and (10); $D = 0$ for $Ex = (Ev+f_c)t*$, or: $t = t* = x/(v+f_c/E)$.
For $t > t_*$: $D = 0$ and also $f_c = 0$.
With $E = A/v$, (16) gives the linear Zarmi recession, Equation 26d.

A.2 Numerical Example of Non-Linear Kinematic-Wave Recession (Table 3.4, Experiment 1).

Step 1: Apply Equation 44 to find $D(l,0)$ with: $p = 1.6500 \ 10^{-5}$ m s^{-1}, $f_c = 0.1333$ 10^{-5} m/s, $l = 12.50$ m, $m = 1.0$, and $K = 0.0801$ m s^{-1}:
$D(l,0) = (1.6500 - 0.1333)10^{-5} \ 12.50/0.0801 = 2.3669 \ 10^{-3}$ m.

Step 2: Now use Equation 44 to find K for $m = 3/2$:
$K(m = 3/2) = (1.6500 - 0.1333)10^{-5} \ 12.50/(2.3669 \ 10^{-3})^{3/2} = 1.6464$.
The recession curve is determined for $q = 1.6464 \ D^{3/2}$ m^{2}s^{-1}.

Step 3: Recession starts from $q(l,0) = 1.6464 \ (2.3669 \ 10^{-3})^{3/2}$,
or: $Q(l,0) = wq(l,0) = 10.00 \times 0.1896 = 1.896 \ 10^{-3}$ m3 s^{-1}.

Step 4: Now select a wave depth (e.g. $D_0 = 2.2000 \ 10^{-3}$ m) less than water depth, $D(l,0)$, at the start of recession.
Apply Equation 45 to find the position, x_0, of the selected wave depth:
$x_0 = 1.6464 \ (0.0022)^{3/2}/(1.6500 - 0.1333)10^{-5} = 11.2013$ m.

Step 5: Use Equation 51 to find the time, t_l, required for the point at selected wave depth, D_0, to reach the end of the plane, $x = l$:
$12.50 = 11.2013 + (1.6464/0.1333 \ 10^{-5})[0.0022^{3/2} - (0.0022 - 0.1333 \ 10^{-5} \ t_l)^{3/2}]$, which gives: $t_l = 11.2$ s.

Step 6: The water depth, $D(l,t_l)$, follows from Equation 42:
$D(l,11.2) = 0.0022 - (0.1333\ 10^{-5}\ 11.2) = 2.1851\ 10^{-3}$ m.

Step 7: Apply (14) to calculate the flow rate:
$q(l,11.2) = 1.6464\ (2.1851\ 10^{-3})^{3/2} = 0.1682\ 10^{-3}$ m^2 s^{-1} and the discharge: $Q(l,11.2)$
$= wq(l,11.2) = 1.682\ 10^{-3}$ m^3 s^{-1}. The next point of the recession curve is: (11.2 s,
$1.682\ 10^{-3}$ m^3 s^{-1}).
Return to Step 4, select new D_0, and repeat Steps 4, 5, 6, and 7.